THE GAS INDUSTRY
Today and Tomorrow

LESLIE T. MINCHIN
B.Sc., M.I.Gas E., F.Inst.F.

GEORGE G. HARRAP & CO. LTD
London · Toronto · Wellington · Sydney

First published in Great Britain 1966
by GEORGE G. HARRAP & CO. LTD
182 High Holborn, London, W.C.1

© *Leslie T. Minchin* 1966
Copyright. All rights reserved

TO MY WIFE, ELAINE

c

234899
Ind. Econ.

*Composed in Monotype Times and printed at
the Pitman Press, Bath
Made in Great Britain*

Foreword

by

SIR HENRY JONES, K.B.E.

Chairman, The Gas Council

In this book the author provides a very useful record of the present activities of the gas industry in Great Britain. In the closing chapter he gives his impression of the shape of things to come. Efficient fuel and energy supplies are essential for a modern industrial country, and this easily read volume contains a great deal of information of value to those working in, or interested in, their provision. It is written in a way that makes it informative and pleasant reading for the general reader.

List of Plates

Contents

1 | Two Notable Occasions

The first public use of coal gas was on June 4th, 1805, in St James's Park, London. At that time the commercial use of an inflammable gas, and its conveyance through pipes, was quite novel. Several observant and ingenious men had already noticed that wood or coal, when heated in a closed chamber, emitted an inflammable vapour. They had even demonstrated that this could be used as a light source, or as a filling for balloons. But the notion that this 'inflammable air' might be developed on a large scale as a public supply was completely new.

However, on this June day in 1805 an enterprising gentleman called Mr Winsor had installed a 'carbonizing furnace' in the garden of his Pall Mall house. Here an iron vessel filled with coal was heated over a fire, and a long pipe made of tinned iron, with soldered joints, carried off the inflammable vapours for a distance of some 300 yards to the top of the wall separating Carlton House Gardens from St James's Park. The occasion was the royal birthday, and the lighted gas jets on the wall illuminated "a number of cut-glass jars and other devices, with gas lights behind each, besetting the crown and letters G.R."

A contemporary journalist described the reaction of the Londoners to this remarkable experiment:

> The light produced by these gas lamps was clear, bright and colourless, and from the success of this considerable experiment hopes may now be entertained that this long-talked-of mode of lighting our streets may at length be realized. The Mall continued crowded with spectators until nearly twelve aclock, and they seemed much amused and delighted by this novel exhibition.

They were witnessing the very first public use of coal gas, and of a form of lighting which—though very poor by present-day standards —was an immense improvement on anything which had been known previously.

During the next 159 years the gas industry grew and developed into a nationwide service. Its role gradually changed from the provision of illumination to the supply of heat in the home, the office, and the factory. The industry spread overseas—a great many gasworks abroad were built and owned by enterprising British gas engineers in the first half of the nineteenth century. In America the development followed a similar pattern, until during the 1920s manufactured gas began to be displaced by a new product, natural gas, which could be extracted from boreholes in the rocks. Although the first gas wells became exhausted as time went on, more new ones were continually being discovered. Instead of the supply failing, the gas became more and more abundant.

This brings us to the second of our two notable occasions, the date of which was October 12th, 1964. On that day a most unusual ship, the *Methane Princess*, sailed into the Thames estuary and docked at Canvey Island, near Southend-on-Sea. It carried a cargo of liquefied natural gas, a liquid which must be maintained at a temperature of −162°C (nearly as cold as liquid air) if it is not to boil away.

The natural gas had originated in a bare tract of the Sahara desert, where boreholes had previously been drilled deep into the rock and a huge store of gas had been discovered. Pipelines had carried it to the Mediterranean coast, where it had been liquefied in a new plant specially built for this purpose. The super-cold liquid was transferred to the heavily insulated tanks in the ship's hold, and in this manner it was conveyed to the Thames. At Canvey another completely new installation was awaiting the arrival of the *Methane Princess*, so that the liquid could be pumped off to the tanks on shore and stored until needed. Probably it would not remain there for long, for a special pipeline had already been constructed across England to convey the gas to a dozen centres of population, lying between the Thames and the Mersey.

These two historical events, one in 1805 and one in 1964, can be taken as forming a frame within which we shall try to set the whole story of the gas industry, though fresh events may happen while this book is in preparation which take us outside these time limits. The story begins, as we have seen, in that exciting half-century between 1775 and 1825 which saw not only an immense upheaval in the thoughts and beliefs of European man but also the birth of the gas industry and three further inventions—the steam engine, the railway, and the electric motor and generator. Although the gas and the electricity industries both sprang from this half-century, the public supply of electricity came much later than that of gas.

After 1805 the commercial use of the inflammable vapours derived from the heating of coal in closed retorts grew to be an important part of civilized life in most parts of the globe. It developed most fully in cool climates where there was an abundant coal supply —notably in Great Britain. In countries such as Switzerland or Norway, where coal had to be imported (and mountains were plentiful), the hydroelectric industry could produce power which was as cheap as or cheaper than that provided by coal gas. However, even in such circumstances fuel gas still had some specific advantages and a relatively small gas industry grew up there too.

Power, in one form or another, is an essential to civilized man; indeed, many people reckon the degree of civilization by the units of power available per head of the population. Without it, men are limited to the tasks which human or animal muscles can perform. A form of power which can be conveyed automatically into the home or the factory, and which can be drawn off at the turn of a tap or switch, has become a basic necessity.

We speak of power, but we could almost as well talk of heat. The power supplied to a dwelling is mostly needed in the form of heat: to raise the temperature of the living space, to provide warm water, and to cook food. In addition, power is needed to drive a variety of small mechanisms—vacuum cleaners, gramophones, radio and television sets—and to provide illumination at night time. In the factory heat is needed to manufacture goods; this means heat in furnace or boiler, and motive power to drive the machinery.

Before either gas or electricity were available, solid fuels were practically the only source of power. Harnessed to the steam engine, they made the Industrial Revolution possible and freed shipping from its dependence on the wind. The steam engine rapidly declined in importance as the liquid mineral fuel, petroleum, entered into our lives. Used with a light and reliable engine, it gives us a most valuable source of transportable power—it has indeed become almost indispensable for vehicles.

Power, then, we must have; for civilized man it has become almost as important as food and drink. Today we rely mostly on the wealth stored up in the earth's crust—coal, petroleum, and natural gas. By using these fuels mankind is living on its capital, for they have taken millions of years to form and we are going to use them up in a century or two. There are two exceptions to this rather melancholy reflection. Solar energy flowing on to the earth in a continuous stream can be utilized directly in the sunnier parts of the earth; it is also used indirectly in hydroelectric plant, for the rain or snow falling on the mountains has been evaporated from the sea by the sun's warmth.

The second exception, likely to be the most important in the future, is nuclear energy; this came into man's hands just at the moment when he was wondering how he would be able to live when the earth's mineral stores had been exhausted. It seems likely that nuclear energy will be able to take over when our coal, petroleum, and gas have been used up.

It will be at least a hundred years, and probably much longer, before we reach this state of affairs; new mineral fuel resources are being discovered at a much faster rate than existing resources are depleted. In this respect there has been a most striking change in the situation of recent years.

Up to the mid-1950s it seemed obvious that Europe at least was heading for an acute fuel shortage. Coal mines, because they were getting older and deeper and less productive, had difficulty in increasing their output, and charts of national energy consumption showed a steady rise in demand year by year. It seemed that in the 1960s the curve of demand was likely to cross the curve of supply; industry would then, it was feared, begin to wilt for lack of energy.

Never was a prophecy so wide of the mark; for the mid-1960s have brought a glut of fuel instead of scarcity. This dramatic change in the situation was due largely to the great increase in the production of petroleum and natural gas, much of it drawn from areas where its existence was barely suspected when the forecast was made. As far as natural gas is concerned, the new fields which have affected Europe most are in Algeria, Western France, Italy, and Holland.

THE GAS FLAME

In this book we shall examine the gas industry, starting with the methods of producing gas, and going on to deal with its storage and distribution, before we come to the gas flame and its uses in home and factory. It is important, however, to have at the outset a clear mental picture of the goal.

Gas is made to be burned. The whole object of the industry is to deliver the gaseous fuel to a selected point where heat is needed; at that point the flame destroys the gas, so that the potential heat it has been carrying can be quickly converted into actual heat; its energy is liberated on the spot, to serve the user's needs in that immediate situation.

The amount of potential heat in a gas is the calorific value; this can vary between 100 British Thermal Units (or Btu) per cubic foot (in producer-gas) and over 3000 (in butane, or L.P. Gas).

There are broadly four types of fuel gas being distributed commercially:

1. Manufactured gas (calorific value about 500 Btu/cu. ft): this usually has at least 40 per cent of hydrogen and varying amounts of carbon monoxide, methane, and other hydrocarbons. It is commonly made from coal, or it may be made from a petroleum derivative and adjusted to resemble coal gas in its properties.
2. Natural gas (calorific value about 1000 Btu/cu. ft): this is mostly methane, but may contain heavier hydrocarbons, nitrogen, and carbon dioxide in addition.
3. Liquefiable petroleum gases (calorific value about 3000 Btu/cu. ft)—often shortened to the letters L.P.G. These are hydrocarbon gases belonging to the same family as methane (paraffins) but of higher molecular weight. L.P. gases usually come from oil wells, gas wells, or oil refineries, and they have one very valuable property: they can be liquefied by pressure alone at ordinary room temperatures. For this reason they are also known as bottled gas, for the relatively light cylinders in which they are stored usually contain the liquid and gas phases together—as the gas is used, the liquid boils to replace it.
4. A mixture of L.P. gases with air. A proportion of about 1 to 4 is usually employed, having a calorific value of about 750 Btu/cu. ft.

In the countries where natural gas is really plentiful it is distributed unchanged; in the United States and the Soviet Union therefore we are only likely to find gas of the second and third families. Britain and the other European countries have traditionally used gas of the first family; parts of France, Italy, Holland, and some East European countries, however use natural gas direct, and where there are reliable and extensive reserves of methane, the process of changing over will continue.

Changing from one type of gas supply to another is a formidable undertaking, however; it usually means that every single gas-burning appliance must be altered. Some of the problems arising are discussed in the last chapter, which deals with the future of the gas industry.

2 | Gas that is Made

Coal carbonization was the main method used to make gas during the first century and a half of the gas industry's existence, although during this time other methods (using coke and oil) were used to provide a supplementary gas, especially at times of peak demand. As recently as 1958 coal formed the source of 90 per cent of all the gas sold in Great Britain, though (as we shall see later in this chapter) this percentage has been falling steadily in recent years.

The basic idea of coal carbonization probably originated with the simple experiment of putting powdered coal in a long clay pipe. The bowl is closed with a plug of clay and is then placed in a fire. As it becomes hot, inflammable tarry vapours will begin to emerge from the mouthpiece of the pipe. They can be lit, and will burn with a bright yellow flame so long as the coal gas continues to be evolved from the coal.

The process is often called 'distillation', but 'destructive distillation' would be more correct. The complex organic molecules of the various substances of which coal is made up are decomposed and give rise to a mixture of:

hydrogen, carbon monoxide, carbon dioxide, methane and a small amount of higher paraffins, ethylene and higher olefines, benzene and other aromatic hydrocarbons and phenols, hydrogen sulphide, ammonia, organic sulphur compounds, naphthalene, tars, and nitrogen.

This list is not exhaustive, of course; one could fill several pages with all the other chemical substances that occur in very small proportions.

VILLAGE GASWORKS

A typical feature of English rural life was the village gasworks, which only began to disappear in the middle years of the twentieth century. Today, most of them have been closed down, but the site usually survives, sheltering a few small gasholders amongst the trees.

How did the village gasworks carry out its function? It was a small-scale industrial process almost as dependent on human muscle as the smithy or the wheelwright's shop. Coal was brought to the site in waggons, by rail or road, and piled up in the yard. From here it was collected as required and taken by hand-barrow to the retort house—a rather grimy building which belched smoke at intervals. Inside the retort house was a large furnace built of brick, from which projected the mouths of a number of horizontal fireclay tubes about 3 feet wide and perhaps 15 feet long.

In cross-section each retort was shaped like a D, with the flat side at the bottom. The mouth of each retort was closed by a heavy door which had to be opened each time a fresh charge of coal was inserted. Beneath the retorts was a large coke fire which raised them to white heat. The stoker, a skilled man of great strength and powers of endurance, inserted the coal in the retort by using a long-handled scoop. He twisted it deftly when it was inside, so that he could withdraw the scoop leaving a layer of coal in the retort. He only filled it to about one half of its capacity, and then he closed the door and left it shut for a period of 8 or 10 hours.

In this process the coal in the retort turns to coke and emits gas. At an early stage it becomes viscous, like black treacle, and the gases being evolved blow it up into a sticky, spongy mass. This stage only lasts a short time, for with further heating the coal (or coke) hardens again. Look carefully at a piece of coke and you can see that it is full of bubbles which have hardened. The gases evolved from the coal pass out through a pipe in the roof of the retort. At this stage they are known as crude gas because they contain tar and many other substances which must be removed before the gas can be passed on to the customer.

At the end of the prescribed period of time the stoker opens the door. He does this quickly, after first loosening it and lighting the gas to let it burn away round the door. He swings the door open, exposing to view the mass of cherry-red coke which now nearly fills the retort—for, in changing to coke, the volume has nearly doubled. Now the stoker inserts a 'rake'—a flat plate at right angles to a long handle—and pulls the coke out. As it falls out of the mouth of the retort it drops into a barrow placed to receive it.

The coke is quenched with water and wheeled away; some of it is used to replenish the fire, and the rest is available for sale. The stoker refills the retort, closes the door, and another charge begins to evolve gas. Meanwhile the crude gas which has been evolved is passing through a series of purification processes. The tar is filtered off, usually by bubbling the gas through water. It then passes to the ammonia washers, where most of the ammonia gas is dissolved out. The 'ammonia liquor' which is obtained contains a great many other chemical substances besides ammonia, but the gasworks hopes to sell it to a chemical factory where the ammonia will be recovered, and probably converted into ammonium sulphate.

There remain two more stages of purification: the gas is washed with oil to remove naphthalene (which would otherwise clog the pipes) and passes through a series of 'purifier boxes' in which it is exposed to a special iron oxide material which reacts with the hydrogen sulphide in the gas. These boxes take up a good deal of room; in fact, they are one of the most conspicuous features of the works. The gas then passes to a storage gasholder and thence to the customers, flowing on its way through a station meter which measures the volume, and governors which control the pressure.

TWO INDUSTRIES

Strangely enough, the carbonization of coal has been undertaken not by one but by two industries: the coke makers who wanted to make coke for iron smelting, and the gas makers who wanted to obtain gas as a fuel. The first of these processes was the earlier; it was in 1721 that coke was first made from coal by Abram Darby in Coalbrookdale. He allowed the surplus gas to escape, and coke makers continued to waste much of their gas until well into the twentieth century.

The gas industry grew up quite independently, without (it would seem) any reference to the coking industry. The gas makers originally regarded coke as a waste product, but later found it to be a secondary fuel of considerable value: coke burns without smoke and it gives a higher thermal efficiency than coal in most solid-fuel appliances.

The two industries maintain their separate identity even today. The coke makers carry out carbonization in 'coke ovens' and the gas makers in 'retorts'. However, the surplus gas from the coke ovens is commonly sold to a gas undertaking today, and the coke

B

produced by the gas makers finds a big market as a household and industrial fuel. The type of carbonizing plant known as 'a battery of coke ovens' is also used by one or two large gasworks.

VERTICAL RETORTS

The most typical coal carbonizing plant in a gasworks today, however, is the vertical retort. In this the charge moves steadily down a hot oval tube. It is fed in as coal at the top and it emerges as coke at the bottom. Fig. 1 shows this kind of plant in diagrammatic section. A number of such retorts are built into a block of fire-resistant brickwork, provided with many channels through which burning gases can circulate. In this way the whole mass of brickwork around each retort is heated to about 1300°C.

As the charge nears the bottom of the retort it is cooled with steam, so that the coke can easily be removed by a screw extraction mechanism and needs no further quenching. The steam passes up through the red-hot coke and there reacts with it to produce some water-gas (H_2 and CO). This mixes with the coal gas, and all the gases leave by the offtake pipe at the top.

The gas used to heat the vertical retorts is burned with air. By controlling the amount of air admitted at various points the most desirable temperature distribution can be achieved. The gas used for this purpose is not coal gas but producer-gas made in a nearby producer or generator.

PRODUCERS

In a producer the solid fuel (usually coke) is gasified—that is, it is turned into a gas without leaving any solid residue apart from ash (the incombustible mineral matter).

When coke burns in an open fire the oxygen is normally in abundant supply, and is able to convert almost all the carbon into carbon *di*oxide. Even so, there will usually be parts of the fuel bed where there is less oxygen, and here you will see a blue flame flickering above the red-hot coke. This indicates that carbon *mon*oxide has been formed, and is burning subsequently with more air to form carbon dioxide.

In a producer the process is arrested at the carbon monoxide stage. By altering the proportions of the fuel bed, and carefully controlling the volume of air admitted, the coke can be made to

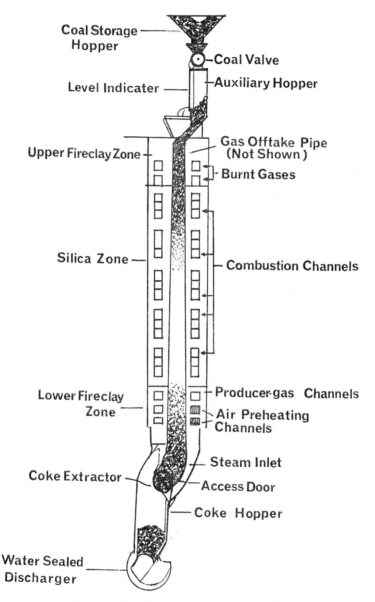

Fig. 1. Cross-section through a continuous vertical retort.

burn mostly to carbon monoxide; this, together with the nitrogen of the air which went into the plant, and a small amount of carbon dioxide and hydrogen, constitutes producer-gas. The hydrogen comes from small amounts of water which enter into the reaction— sometimes this comes from the grate and sometimes it is added deliberately.

The chemical reactions are very simple:

(1) Coke fire $C + O_2 \rightarrow CO_2$ (system gets hotter)
(2) Producer $2C + O_2 \rightarrow 2CO$ (system gets hotter)
(3) Reaction with $C + H_2O \rightarrow CO + H_2$ (system gets cooler)
    water or steam

Naturally, a certain amount of carbon dioxide (CO_2) is formed even when it is not desired.

Reaction 2 proceeds with the evolution of heat; it is a kind of incomplete burning. This is how producer-gas is made. In a retort installation the producer-gas is usually conveyed still hot to the channels where it is to be burned. In this way most of the heat which could be obtained by burning coke is obtained in a form that can be applied efficiently and accurately to the object to be heated; a far better method than by direct contact with the burning coke.

COKE OVENS

As we have seen, the manufacture of coke (with gas as a by-product) has developed on rather different lines from the manufacture of gas (with coke as a by-product). A great deal of coke is needed for use in blast furnaces; there it combines with the oxygen of the iron ore so that metallic iron is liberated. For this purpose special qualities of coke are needed, rather different from the kind of coke needed for the domestic fire. In particular, it must be mechanically strong, so that it is not crushed by the weight of the charge above it in the blast furnace.

The coke ovens which have been developed for the production of this metallurgical coke are basically similar to the retorts used in the gasworks, but are different in shape. The coke oven is a vertical slab about 2 feet thick, and perhaps 14 feet high and 30 feet long. A battery of coke ovens consists of twenty or thirty such chambers, side by side, like a multiple sandwich, built into a solid block of

PLATE 1. BP's 8,500 ton drilling platform *Sea Quest*, seen under tow after her successful flotation at the Belfast yard of Harland and Wolff on January 7th, 1966. *Sea Quest* is to be used in the search for gas and oil in the North Sea.

(*A BP Photograph*)

PLATE 2. The Pall Mall gas lights in 1805, as seen in a contemporary drawing.

fireproof masonry, with flame channels in between each chamber to provide the heating.

At each end, the oven is closed by rectangular steel and firebrick doors, which are only opened when the charge has been fully carbonized and is ready to be discharged. The oven is then 'pushed': a steel ram is forced into the oven from one side, causing a wall of red-hot coke to emerge from the other end. This can be a spectacular sight, especially on a gloomy day! As it comes out, the wall of flaming coke crumbles and breaks up, falling on to a sloping floor known as the wharf, whence it slides into waiting trucks.

A locomotive moves the steel trucks full of red-hot flaming coke and places them in position under a quenching tower. Here a deluge of water pours on to the hot coke, a cloud of steam ascends to the heavens, and the quenched coke, still in its truck, is moved off to be mechanically sorted into different sizes and heaped in the storage hoppers. Many systems of 'dry-quenching' have been developed which put the heat to useful purpose, instead of wasting it as is done at the quenching tower. Although from a technical point of view such a development is obviously desirable, the plant is expensive and has not been widely adopted.

Originally, such coke ovens were always heated by some of the coal gas which was diverted for the purpose; the remainder was often just burned at an open pipe—wasted. Nowadays that is not likely to happen in an advanced country, for the gas can be sold with advantage to a gas undertaking, or used (especially at steelworks) for the firing of metallurgical furnaces in another part of the same site.

In Britain, many of the coke-oven batteries are owned by the National Coal Board and are situated near the collieries. Usually the total output of gas is sold to the area gas board, and the heating of the coke ovens is by producer-gas or (as at Wath-on-Dearne, near Doncaster) by methane which has been extracted from coal mines in the neighbourhood (see Chapter 3).

GASIFICATION OF COAL: WATER-GAS

So far, we have mainly discussed the manufacture of gas from coal by carbonization—that is, by the heating of coal in a closed retort or chamber. The other method, known in the industry as complete gasification, has been briefly mentioned in connection with the producer-gas used in retort houses.

Carbonization is a technique which produces not one fuel, but two: gas and coke. The gas industry in the past has had the task of balancing the supply of these two fuels and this has sometimes proved difficult; in times of general prosperity the demand for coke tends to fall and that for gas tends to rise. Thus for many years past, although the industry was based on carbonization, methods were in use for varying the proportions in which gas and coke were produced.

The water-gas process was used for this purpose, and it was also extremely useful for meeting sudden increases in the demand for gas. In the water-gas process air and steam are alternately blown through a large cylinder full of coke. The gas-making reaction for the action of steam on red-hot coke is shown in the third equation on page 20. Because this extracts heat from the system, making it progressively cooler, it is necessary to stop the steam and blow air instead for a while, to heat up the coke bed again; during this part of the cycle the burned gases are blown to the atmosphere.

Naturally, the actual process is a good deal more complicated than the last paragraph would suggest. The mixture of hydrogen and carbon monoxide has a heating value of only about 300 British Thermal Units per cubic foot (or 2900 kilocalories per cubic metre), which is much lower than coal gas. Since it is usually necessary to produce a gas with a heating value of about 500, arrangements are made to spray oil on to red-hot bricks inside another cylindrical chamber; the oil breaks up into gaseous hydrocarbons which enrich the water gas. It is then known as carburetted water-gas. There are several boilers at different points in the plant which generate steam from heat which would otherwise be wasted; commonly they make enough steam to supply all the needs of the gas-making phase.

GASIFICATION OF COAL: MORE RECENT PROCESSES

In the years which followed the Second World War the European gas industry began to search for ways by which it could emancipate itself from its dependence on coal carbonization. In the United States of America, and one or two other countries, the discovery of large natural gas reserves in the earth's crust had already made carbonization obsolete.

There were perhaps three important reasons for this tendency to move away from carbonization, even when using coal:

(a) The difficulty of balancing gas supply against coke supply, and the declining demand for coke.

(b) Shortage of good gas-making coals. Not every coal is suitable for carbonization; many coals do not produce a coherent coke, but give rise to a sort of coke dust which is difficult to handle and harder still to sell. Coals which have a good gas yield, and also produce good-quality coke, only constitute about 38 per cent of the output in Britain. (1948 figures.)

(c) The developing ideas of transmission by long-distance pipeline pointed to the advantage of making gas in large units close to the coal mine. Gas can be transported much more cheaply than coal.

The first complete gasification systems, designed to convert coal completely into gas, were cyclic in operation, and followed closely the pattern of the water-gas process just described. Steam was blown through the coal for a few minutes, making hydrogen and carbon monoxide, in addition to the hydrocarbons and tar obtained by distilling the coal.

This cooled the fuel bed, so the steam had to be interrupted and air blown through it; this raised the temperature again and prepared it for the next steam phase. Usually the coal was fed into the top of the retort and stayed at first in a medium temperature zone, giving off hydrocarbon vapours, tar, etc. The air-blow did not pass through this zone, but was confined to the lower part of the retort, where the coal had largely become coke.

Fig. 2 shows a representative of this class. It has been used to a considerable extent in Europe, and it uses a low-grade coal which could never be used in a carbonization plant.

Coal from the bunker A descends into the carbonization zone B which is heated by the hot gases circulating through the passages C. The gases and vapours which distil from the coal pass away through the offtake pipe D. The process changes the coal into coke, which slides down into zone E.

Arriving at E, the hot coke is subjected alternately to steam and air blasts. During the steam period water-gas is made, which passes on to the carburettor (where oil is added) and the superheater

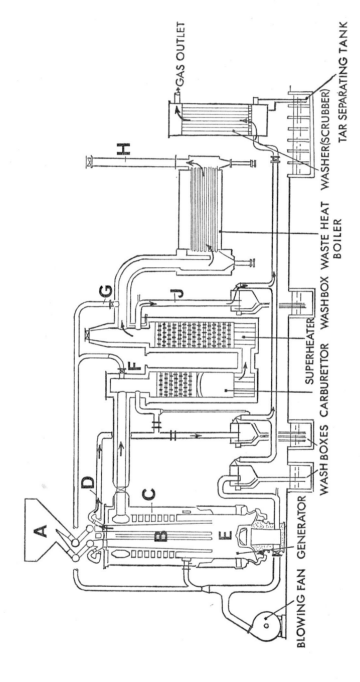

Fig. 2. Diagram of a plant for the gasification of coal at low pressure. (*After Ricketts & Elgin,* 1962.)

GAS OUTLET

H

G

J

F

A

D

C

B

E

BLOWING FAN   GENERATOR

WASH BOXES   CARBURETTOR   WASHBOX   WASTE HEAT   WASHER(SCRUBBER)
SUPERHEATER   BOILER

TAR SEPARATING TANK

(where the decomposition of the oil is completed), and so down pipe J to the gas outlet. As steaming cools the coke bed, an air blast is sent in to warm it up again; the 'blow gases' formed during this period are blown to the atmosphere through H, but only after they have given up most of their heat to the carburettor, the superheater, and finally the waste-heat boiler. The steaming is then renewed, and so the process goes on.

However, cyclic processes of this kind tend to have a rather low thermal efficiency, because inevitably a proportion of the gas made must be rejected with the burned gases from the air-blow phase. Also, they involve a rather cumbersome plant, big and expensive in relation to the output. The next stage therefore was to use oxygen in place of air; this removed the need to heat up large quantities of atmospheric nitrogen, and it also allowed the process to be made continuous. The oxygen could be mixed with the steam, and the two blown in together so that a mixture of coal/water-gas and oxygen/producer-gas was formed.

LURGI PROCESS

In the Lurgi process (Fig. 3) a mixture of oxygen and steam is blown through a mass of coal. This, at ordinary pressures, would just produce a mixture of carbon monoxide and hydrogen, plus a certain amount of hydrocarbons coming from the coal as it was heating up. Such a mixture would still have a lower calorific value[1] than the coal gas to which we are accustomed in most countries. However, by operating the process at a much higher pressure we can encourage the formation of methane. This is formed by a reaction which one can represent (simplifying) as:

$$C + 2H_2 \rightarrow CH_4$$

As each molecule of a gas takes up about the same amount of space, this kind of reaction represents a reduction in volume; two volume units of hydrogen turn to one volume unit of methane. A well-known principle in chemistry lays it down that reactions leading to a reduction of volume are favoured by increase of pressure; and this is certainly true of methane formation in gasification processes.

The use of high pressures (about 22 atmospheres is usual) not only increases the methane content, and therefore the calorific value

---

[1] See Table 2, Chapter 8.

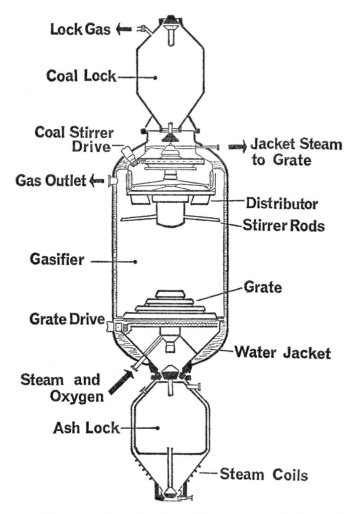

Lock Gas

Coal Lock

Coal Stirrer Drive

Jacket Steam to Grate

Gas Outlet

Distributor

Stirrer Rods

Gasifier

Grate

Grate Drive

Water Jacket

Steam and Oxygen

Ash Lock

Steam Coils

Fig. 3. Diagrammatic section through the generator of a Lurgi plant for gasifying coal under pressure. Stirring rods are provided to prevent the formation of a solid mass of coke. Since the gasifier operates at high pressure, the addition of coal at the top and the withdrawal of ash at the bottom must be done through a lock system (like a canal lock). The gasifier is surrounded by a water-jacket to preserve the metal structure, and the steam formed is used in the process.

of the gas; it also has other advantages. It means that all the vessels and pipes can be very much smaller; carbon dioxide can be removed by simply washing with water or potassium carbonate solution; and at the end of the process the gas is available at high pressure for discharging into long-distance mains without any further pumping.

The Lurgi process is only economic if operated in very large units. The largest in the world, the SASOL plant in South Africa, consumes over 3000 tons of coal every day when at full production; the smaller Westfield plant in Fifeshire (Scotland) takes 630 tons. In each case the coal comes from an adjacent coal mine by conveyor belt.

Although the Lurgi process seemed to offer great advantages when it was introduced, producing gas at about 15 per cent less cost than by carbonization processes, it has been overtaken in its turn by other still more advantageous processes for making gas from oil. One inherent weakness of all coal-using processes is that much energy is consumed in handling solids. At one Lurgi plant the cost of electricity (for power) was about the same as the cost of the coal used for gas making. Another disadvantage is that the capital cost of the Lurgi plant is very high, and, as we have seen, the demand for gas is becoming more and more seasonal in character.

GAS MANUFACTURE FROM PETROLEUM PRODUCTS

As we saw in Chapter 1, mankind today is largely relying on the 'bank balance' of fossil fuels stored up in the earth's crust. These fossil fuels are principally coal, oil, and gas. From its early days until quite recently the gas industry made its gas from coal, but now the emphasis is rapidly shifting (in Western Europe) in favour of petroleum products.

This change can be attributed to a number of causes. In the first place coal (and especially gas-making coal) has become much more expensive as it has become less easily accessible. Moreover, the miners, who were at one time scandalously badly paid, are now treated to much better conditions and wages. This has caused coal to become dearer just at the time when more and more reserves of petroleum have been discovered, and substances derived from it have become cheaper.

In the second place, coal-handling and coal-treating plant is very expensive in first cost and upkeep. You have only to compare the cost of running a conveyor belt for coal with that of a pipeline for oil; obviously the pipe is a simpler and cheaper device. The Lurgi plant costs about five times as much as an installation for making the same amount of gas from oil. If the demand for gas were the same in summer as in winter this might not be so serious (if for instance gas were used only for cooking and water heating), but when the demand in winter is three times as much as in summer, then a great deal of gas-making plant must stand idle for much of the year. Capital costs then become very important.

A third factor is that modern gas-making plants using petroleum products are far more versatile. They can be fed with the light petroleum fraction often called 'naphtha', or they can take natural gas (if and when it becomes available), and a third alternative is the L.P. gas (see next chapter) which can be stored in light metal tanks and is invaluable in an emergency. In countries which already have a supply of natural gas, and hope to have more in future, oil gasification plants can be designed to provide a gas very similar to methane.

Petroleum, of course, is a complex mixture of hydrocarbons. These can be separated from one another by distillation, or rather the components which have boiling points close together can be separated from those having much higher or much lower boiling points. Such a group of similar hydrocarbons is called a 'fraction'. For example, the petroleum technologist may say of an oil that "the fraction boiling between 50°C and 100°C is 25 per cent".

At all times some fractions have been more in demand than others. In the very early days it was the middle fraction, kerosene (or paraffin) that was valuable for its use in oil lamps. Then came the age of the motor car, and the light fraction known as petrol or gasoline was in greatest demand. The heavy oil was used for lubrication and the medium-heavy was least in demand—the gas industry bought it as 'gas oil' for use in water-gas plants. Today the position has again changed. So much diesel fuel is used for locomotion, and kerosene-type oil for jet engines, that the light fraction is now the most plentiful.

Nearly all the gas-making plants being built in Britain at the time this book is being written are designed to make use either of L.P. gas or of the light petroleum fraction (naphtha or primary flash distillate), as this is the cheapest raw material available today.

PLATE 3. The *Methane Princess*, which carries liquid methane from Africa to England.

PLATE 4. The village gasworks. This little factory at Wildenhall, Suffolk, supplied about 400 households.

Gas made from it is even cheaper than natural gas transported to Britain from Algeria in liquid form (see Chapter 5), but the commercial position is liable to change, and may be different by the time these lines are being read.

OIL GASIFICATION

The principle of the oil gasification processes strongly resembles that of the coal gasification methods we have just been describing. Indeed the three equations given on page 20 are broadly applicable —it being understood that for C one puts C_xH_y to stand for a variety of hydrocarbons. It follows that some H_2O or H_2 must also appear on the right-hand side of the equation.

Of course, one cannot write a precise equation for the process unless one knows just what hydrocarbon is being treated. However, it remains generally true that combustion, whether complete (as in equation 1) or incomplete (equation 2), generates heat, while the steam reaction (equation 3) usually absorbs heat. Oxygen, in the form of air, is the cheapest reagent possible; it also gives rise to reactions which are self-sustaining, and need no heat from outside. Against these advantages must be set the fact that the air is four-fifths nitrogen, and you are liable to end up with a fuel gas which contains a large amount of this inert substance, which is not easily removed. Oxygen can be separated from nitrogen by liquefaction, but then it is no longer a cheap reagent.

Any process using a heat-absorbing reaction starts with a certain disadvantage, for the loss of heat must be made good either by making the process into a cyclic one (as in the water-gas process) or else by supplying heat through the walls of the reaction vessel. This latter alternative is usually preferred, since it makes possible operation at high pressure.

In practice some steam is nearly always used, because otherwise it is difficult to avoid forming solid carbon in the reaction. One of the first successful processes carried the strange name of ONIA-GEGI—a name formed from the initials of the two companies which collaborated in its development.

Fig. 4 shows in simplified form the ONIA-GEGI plant. The actual gas making takes place in vessel C. Steam and the hydrocarbon to be used are introduced at the top, and they pass down through a mass of catalytic material K which encourages the chemical reaction between them. The hydrocarbon molecules are broken up, producing a mixture of hydrogen, carbon monoxide, and methane which passes off to the right through a washbox designed to trap any tar or carbon that may have been formed.

This gas-making operation absorbs heat, and so after a certain time (10 minutes perhaps) it is stopped and oil is burned at A. Some air is added by pipe G and more through H, so that there is some free oxygen in the hot gases which sweep through the catalyst chamber C and they burn off any carbon which may have formed

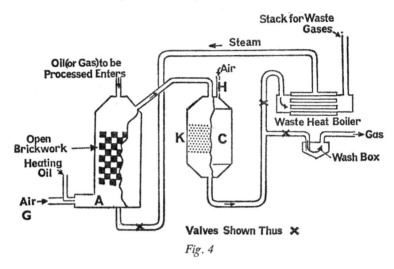

Fig. 4

there. This operation not only cleans the chamber but also heats it, until it is ready for a fresh gas-making phase.

The use of a catalyst must be mentioned here, because these substances assume even greater importance in the newer methods about to be described. The catalyst is usually a metallic oxide (such as nickel oxide) which is made up into pellets and has the valuable property of accelerating the speed of certain chemical reactions. Oil vapour and steam at this temperature would react very slowly if no catalyst were present, and very large vessels would be needed. The catalyst can also be chosen to encourage certain reactions more than others, and in this way the chemical change desired can be made more rapid, and will take place at lower temperatures than would otherwise be needed.

PRESSURE METHODS OF OIL GASIFICATION

Most of the installations being built today are designed to work at high pressure, and this has resulted in a move away from cyclic processes. (It would be most undesirable for a high pressure vessel to be vented to the atmosphere every few minutes.) Instead, the catalyst masses are placed in tubes made of very high-grade stainless steel and these are usually heated outside by burning some convenient fuel.

Many different and slightly different processes have been developed for gasifying hydrocarbons in steam; in Britain one of the most widely used is the I.C.I. steam/naphtha process developed originally as a source of pure hydrogen for chemical synthesis. Several very large units are now in operation making gas for the area gas boards, and producing huge outputs from an area of ground which (compared with classical carbonization methods) seems absurdly small.

Fig. 5 shows the general principle of the steam/naphtha process. The really important part is the catalyst, which is packed in a series of vertical tubes which run from top to bottom of the tubular re-forming[1] furnace. Some unpurified naphtha is burned around the outside of the tubes to supply the heat needed to compensate for the loss of heat caused by the reaction.

Unfortunately, the catalyst is very easily spoiled by traces of sulphur compounds. The first stages of the process are therefore devoted to eliminating organic sulphur compounds, by treating them with some of the hydrogen-rich gas which the process produces. In the case of the simplest organic sulphur compound, carbon disulphide, CS_2, this reaction takes place:

$$4H_2 + CS_2 \rightarrow 2H_2S + CH_4$$

and the H_2S is relatively easy to remove—in this case by zinc oxide. This all takes place in the vapour phase sulphur removal unit, and after this the vapours mix with steam and enter the main reaction tubes already described.

The hot products of combustion leaving the re-forming furnace (from the outside of the tubes) are not allowed to escape until they have given up most of their heat to generate the steam needed by the process. The last stage, as the gas leaves the re-forming tubes (still

---

[1] Re-forming is a rearrangement of the hydrocarbon molecules to produce a combustible gas of suitable composition.

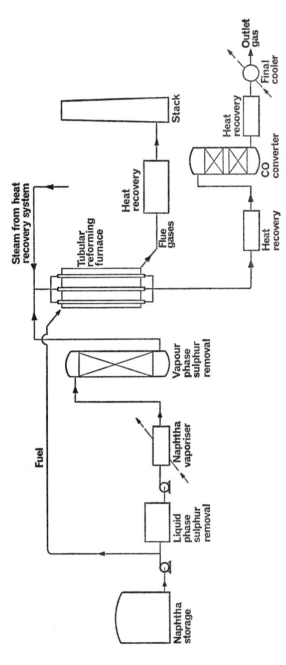

Fig. 5. Diagram of the I.C.I. steam/naphtha process. The catalyst is contained in the vertical tubes running through the tubular reforming furnace.

at 30 atmospheres pressure) is to pass it through the CO converter which makes the gas less toxic. This will be described in more detail in Chapter 6.

Still newer processes are being developed. Particular attention is being given to the manufacture of rich gases (i.e. having a heating value between 500 and 1000 Btu/cu. ft) since the I.C.I. process described above produces a 'lean gas'[1] consisting mostly of hydrogen, carbon dioxide, and a little methane; this must be enriched with a high calorific value gas before it is suitable for distribution to the ordinary gas consumer.

If the works is situated in a place where natural gas or residual gas from an oil refinery is available in quantity, this will obviously be used to enrich the lean gas. Alternatively, there are two new processes (both originating at the Gas Council's Research Station at Solihull, near Birmingham) which can be used to avoid the need for an external source of enrichment.

One of these processes depends upon the hydrogenation of the naphtha—i.e., the addition of hydrogen to it. The hydrogen is derived from a continuous catalytic re-forming plant such as the I.C.I. process just discussed; if the carbon dioxide is removed the result is a gas containing perhaps 80 per cent to 90 per cent H_2. The reaction between this gas and the hydrocarbon proceeds in an unpacked cylinder, without any catalyst; it liberates heat, and care has to be taken that it does not become too hot. The hydrogenation process makes a 'rich gas' and thus forms a useful auxiliary to the catalytic re-forming technique.

Even newer is the two-stage re-forming process. This depends basically on the discovery that, whereas the reaction of naphtha with steam was always regarded as requiring heat, this is not true at low temperatures. At 530°C it is slightly heat-producing. This results in a gas rich in methane which is not suitable for ordinary use, so it is passed to a second catalyst chamber where, after addition of air, the percentage of hydrogen increases and carbon monoxide is formed. If the gas stream then passes to a detoxification chamber, the result is a gas quite similar to town gas produced very efficiently and cheaply. It is to be noted that this process has the

---

[1] A recent modification of the I.C.I. process enables it to make ordinary town gas. The Topsøe process (which is similar, but operates at a higher pressure) also produces gas of 500 Btu/cu. ft without enrichment.

C

advantage that it requires no expensive externally heated catalyst chambers.

The two-stage process has yet to be applied on a commercial scale, but it is quite likely that the extremely promising small-scale experiments will have been followed up with a plant on the commercial scale by the time this book appears. Some full-scale plants using the first stage alone are already under construction; the method is then known as the Rich Gas Catalytic Process.

3 | Gas that is Found

The part of the earth's crust accessible to men is only a few miles thick, but it contains an amazing amount of wealth for the folk who walk on top of it.

Some of the minerals, like gold and copper, have been used for many thousands of years. Coal, the first fossil fuel to be utilized, has been dug out of the earth for perhaps eight or nine hundred years—in the Limburg province of Holland, for instance, it is said to have been mined since the year 1100. These early mining operations were only conducted with shallow pits, and of course could only reach the seams which lay just below the surface of the ground.

Around the end of the nineteenth century and the beginning of the twentieth, petroleum began to be produced. This black oily liquid, crude petroleum, had dissolved in it an inflammable gas—mostly methane—which was evolved as soon as the pressure was released. As we mentioned in the last chapter, petroleum consists of a complex mixture of hydrocarbons—compounds of carbon and hydrogen. The lightest and simplest have only one, two, three, or four carbon atoms to the molecule. Their formulae are:

Methane, CH_4 Ethane, C_2H_6 Propane, C_3H_8
Butane, C_4H_{10}

These four compounds are all gases at ordinary temperatures, though the last two (propane and butane) can be liquefied under pressure. All four are dissolved in the crude petroleum, and are normally separated from it at the oil well (though some propane and butane may be left in the oil when it is transported). At first these gases were simply burned, for there was no use for them. Indeed, this still happens today in those parts of the world which are far removed from centres of civilization.

However, in the United States of America petroleum engineers exploiting the Texas oilfields decided to make use of the gas by piping it to the cities and selling it to the local gas companies. This proved a very successful project; before long, oil companies were drilling for gas as well as for oil, and on some sites it was found that only gas, or gas with a small amount of liquids, was obtained. By 1939 pipelines were carrying this 'natural gas' to most of the main cities of the United States, and the manufacture of gas from coal or oil had become of only secondary importance. Coal was, and still is, carbonized in coke ovens for the production of coke needed for iron smelting.

HOW DID IT ORIGINATE?

It is surprising that we know so little about the mechanism by which natural gas was formed in the earth. The most firmly established theory is that both the gaseous and the liquid petroleum products have been formed from organic animal matter deposited on the floor of the ocean some hundreds of million years ago. The decaying bodies of crustaceans have been suggested, but without much supporting evidence. Over this organic material other layers of alluvium were deposited, one of which was destined to become an impervious cap rock at a later stage in the earth's history.

Just as, in the coal measures, wood plus water under the fierce compression of the rocks and the aeons of geological time became coal, plus a certain amount of methane (known to miners as fire-damp); similarly, these organic remains of sea creatures turned to liquid petroleum and to methane. The liquid and the gas were not fixed to the place of generation, however; unlike coal, they could move through some of the rock strata and might eventually, when discovered, be in a porous sandstone some distance from the stratum in which they had been formed. Moreover the gas and the liquid might have migrated to different places, so that although gas is normally found associated with petroleum, it is sometimes non-associated—i.e., occurring by itself.

For example, the big gas field in the Sahara desert, called Hassi-er-R'Mel, is classified as non-associated gas, though a considerable amount of liquid vapours condenses out of the gas when it is treated at the surface. In Holland some gas sources are associated with oil, some are not; and of the latter some are 'wet gas' (i.e. containing

PLATE 5. Modern naphtha re-forming plant at Avonmouth near Bristol.

PLATE 6. A well-head 'Christmas tree'. The one illustrated here is on a small well at Cousland near Edinburgh.

substantial proportions of higher hydrocarbons) and some are 'dry gas' (almost entirely methane with a little ethane).

However, it is not certain that non-associated gas was ever part of a petroleum deposit. It is now generally thought that the gas in the huge field at Slochteren, in Holland, and also the gas lying under the bed of the North Sea, may have originated in coal measures. While some gas is obviously part of a petroleum or coal deposit, it has also been suggested that methane may also be produced by some high-pressure, high-temperature reaction in the earth's crust, from the rock materials which compose it.

Such a reaction could be that of water or steam on metallic carbides. Calcium carbide with water gives acetylene under ordinary conditions; the iron carbide Fe_3C (cementite) which might well occur in the lower regions of the earth reacts with water to give a mixture of methane, ethane, and other hydrocarbons.

On the other hand, methane was probably an important constituent of the earth's atmosphere at some early period in geological time, as today it is known to form an important part of the atmosphere of the outer planets Saturn, Uranus, and Neptune. One can say that methane seems to be part of the primeval stuff of the universe. Some of the natural gas we are now finding may have been trapped there when the earth was first formed.

Another possibility is raised by the discovery that certain of the meteorites which fall on the earth from outer space contain a small percentage of heavy hydrocarbons like asphalt. If such a substance had been present in the original earth matter of our planet, it might well have been 'cracked' into lighter hydrocarbons and methane gas by contact with hot substances inside the earth.

One reason why we know so little about the origins of gas and petroleum is that we know so little about the earth's structure generally. We know almost nothing for certain regarding the planet we live on, except for what lies a few miles below the surface—after that we have to rely on indirect evidence, such as the refraction and reflection of earthquake shocks as they pass from one point on the earth's surface to another. However, informed opinion at the moment seems inclined to think that natural gas and petroleum come basically from two sources: 'biogenic', from decayed living creatures, and 'abiogenic', which probably dates from an earlier period in the history of our planet.

OCCURRENCE

Passing from conjecture to established fact, we can say with certainty that natural gas exists in porous rock strata at a number of widely separated sites. For the gas to have been trapped, and for it to remain in the earth, certain fairly obvious physical features are essential. The gas can only be present in a rock which is sufficiently porous to contain it; there must be space between the granules or interconnecting pores in the mass.

The next pre-requisite is that a non-permeable layer must lie above it—otherwise all the gas would have escaped long ago. Moreover, this non-permeable rock cap must be shaped so that the water which normally lies underneath the petroleum or gas seals off the zone. This means that either the formation must be domed or else there must be some faulting which provides the necessary *trap structure* (see Fig. 6). The pressure of the water from below holds the gas under the concavity formed by the impervious layer, and usually holds it at a high pressure; 100 or 200 atmospheres is quite common. (At Lacq it is 670 atmospheres.)

The gas field therefore contains only a limited amount of gas; it can be drawn upon only so long as there is gas remaining, and, when that has all been taken out, the field is finished—though it may be useful as a potential storage reservoir. When natural gas was first used commercially (in the United States) there was widespread speculation as to whether all the gas reserves would not be exhausted in a relatively short time. Before the war it seemed that in ten to fifteen years the industry would be unable to supply its customers; yet today there is more than ever available.

This is due to the unexpected rate at which new gas fields have been discovered. In fact, new gas reserves have been revealed at a far faster rate than old ones have been used up. The most surprising finds recently have been in the Old World—Europe and adjacent lands. Just after the end of the war Italy began to exploit gas fields in the Po basin, and France set to work to utilize gas reserves at Lacq, in the foothills of the Pyrenees (near Pau).

In 1956 a vast new reserve of gas was discovered at Hassi-er-R'Mel in the Sahara desert, 300 miles south of the Mediterranean shore. In 1962 an even greater reserve was found at Slochteren in Holland (near Groningen), and this transformed the whole situation in Europe quite dramatically. It also led petroleum engineers to consider whether the shallow waters of the North Sea might not prove a fruitful area for drilling.

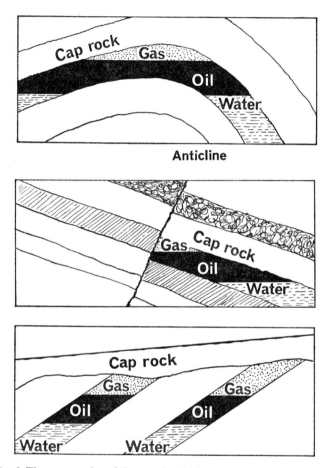

Anticline

Fig. 6. Three examples of the way in which a trap structure can occur in the earth's crust. The anticline, or dome, is the most common.

As we have seen, the occurrence of both oil and gas seems to be associated with the accumulation of organic matter on the bed of shallow prehistoric oceans. It so happens that the ancient ocean known to geologists as the Zechstein Sea (see Fig. 7) covered the gas

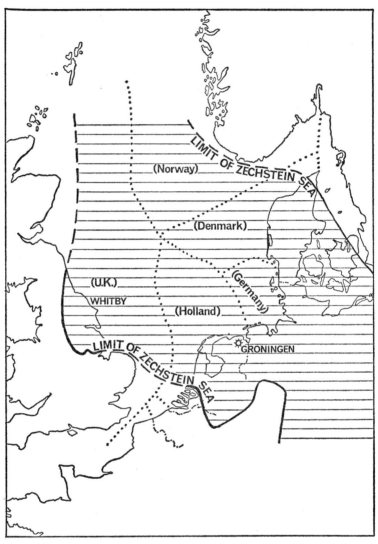

Fig. 7. Map of the North Sea showing the area covered by the Zechstein Sea in Permian times, and the agreed boundaries within which
the several countries can exploit oil and gas.

fields of Holland and North Germany, and this area also includes the only significant British gas field, that of North Yorkshire, near Whitby (even the tiny gas well at Cousland, near Edinburgh, is only just outside the limit).

As can be seen from the map, nearly all the bed of the North Sea is an area in which oil or gas might be found. A considerable amount

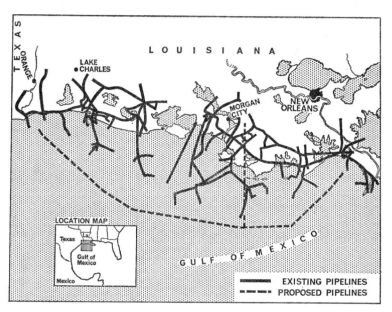

Fig. 8. Map of the Gulf Coast of the Southern U.S.A., showing the pipelines which carry gas and oil from boreholes in the bed of the sea.

of geological exploration has already been carried out, using explosive charges which when detonated produce echoes from the strata underlying the ocean bed. The search was, in the first place, for trap structures which might contain oil or gas. After this, trial drillings were made in the sea bed by drilling from special platforms which are either moored or stand on legs on the sea bottom.

Two successful drillings have already been reported some 40 miles off the English coast, and they are known to contain enough gas to justify commercial exploitation. There is little doubt that more will be discovered as the search proceeds.

The drilling of boreholes in the sea bed is difficult, but by no means impossible. It has been done in other parts of the world with great success—notably in the Gulf of Mexico (off Louisiana), in Lake Maracaibo (Venezuela), and at Abu Dhabi (Persian Gulf). Nearly 2000 million cubic feet of gas are obtained daily in the Gulf of Mexico, where some fifty offshore boreholes are linked up to the mainland by submarine pipelines. The area covered extends 50 to 75 miles from the coastline. It is possible that, by the time this book appears, a new gas reserve as big as Groningen may have been discovered in the North Sea. Already an international agreement has parcelled out the North Sea into national areas, and a good

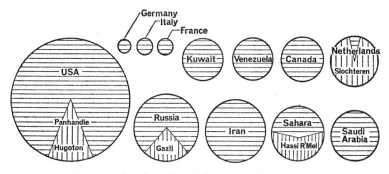

Fig. 9. A diagram showing the relative sizes of natural gas resources in various countries.

deal of importance may attach to whether a strike is made on one side of a line drawn on a map or on the other. (See Fig. 7.)

While these discoveries have been proceeding in the European area there have been important finds in other parts of the world. The natural gas strikes in Alberta have transformed the fuel situation in Canada; pipelines carrying it stretch across the Dominion from coast to coast, and some gas is being exported to the United States as well. Important reserves have been discovered in the Soviet Union, notably the Gazli field which lies south of the Aral Sea and 50 miles north-west of Bokhara. This is thought to hold 500,000 million cubic metres, or 17 billion (10^{12}) cubic feet.

Nearer to Europe, Libya in North Africa has valuable reserves of gas, and these are likely to contribute to the needs of Italy, France, and Spain. Rumania, Hungary, and Poland also have valuable gas fields, and the Communist countries of Eastern Europe generally use natural gas rather than manufactured gas. In Russia the last coal carbonization plant closed down in about 1960.

At the time of writing, Nigeria was the latest country to appear amongst the gas-producing nations; if Nigerian gas is to be utilized, liquefaction plant to transport it must be built (see Chapter 6).

The situation changes so rapidly that it is difficult to give precise figures; but the areas of the circles shown in Fig. 9 are a fair picture of the reserves believed to exist underground in 1964. The segments show the contribution of one single gas field, usually the largest in each country.

DRILLING METHODS

The detailed technique of drilling is outside the scope of this book, but a few observations may be useful.[1] The process is essentially the same as that of drilling through a piece of wood with a brace and bit; the cutting bit is armed with toothed wheels, and this is rotated. However, a factor which makes this kind of drilling very different from the drilling of a hole in a piece of wood is the vast length of drill required. The Hassi-er-R'Mel gas field lies at 7000 feet below the surface, and some wells are deeper than this. Obviously one cannot make a bit of that length, except by joining up a large number of tubes. One of the first things noticed when a drilling rig is seen is that several spare lengths of tubing are hanging inside the pyramidal framework, ready to be used. When one length has passed into the ground, another is joined to it by a screw thread and drilling is resumed.

There are a number of complications to this simple basic idea. For instance, from time to time the bit becomes blunt and must be replaced; this can only be done by pulling up all the lengths of tubing, separating them into lengths which can be handled, and then re-lowering them into the hole after a new bit has been placed on the extreme tip. Again, it is necessary to have a current of drilling fluid (sometimes air) circulating through the system, to bring up to the surface the rock fragments which otherwise would choke the drill.

As the bit approaches a gas reservoir great care has to be exercised, for if the gas bursts through it may get out of control. If this happens,

---

[1] For a good description see George Sell, *The Petroleum Industry* (O.U.P., 1963).

in a very short time one may find a huge flame shooting hundreds of feet into the air in the place where the drilling rig was before; and such a flame is so hot that it is only by very special techniques that anyone can get near it. This actually happened at Lacq, in the south of France, and a long and expensive operation was necessary before it could be brought under control.

The hole in the ground made by the drill must be lined with steel tubing, of course, and on the top of this casing is mounted a group of valves which always goes by the name of the 'Christmas tree'. From here the gas is led (some miles perhaps) to the treatment centre.

NATURAL GAS TREATMENT

Some natural gas contains hydrogen sulphide (H_2S), and this is so corrosive that it must be removed at an early stage. The Lacq gas contains 15 per cent of this gas, and it represented a very serious technical difficulty at first. Some of the H_2S can be removed by washing with water, but the last amounts have to be taken out by washing the gas with one of two organic chemicals—mono- or di-ethylamine. With the large percentage found at Lacq, the sulphur obtained as a by-product is commercially quite important; it has turned France from a sulphur-importing into a sulphur-exporting country.

Nearly always there are heavier hydrocarbon fractions to be removed—substances which are valuable in themselves and which might also prove an embarrassment if they were allowed to condense in long-distance pipelines. One way of removing these fractions is to allow the gas to expand through an orifice. This causes the temperature to fall abruptly, and most of the condensable hydrocarbons are deposited and can be run off. Of course, before it is allowed to expand the gas must first be cooled to the ambient temperature; it usually comes out of the earth hot (100°C or even more).

It is also essential to dry the gas. It comes out of the ground saturated with water vapour, and unless this were removed water would condense in the pipes and create a great nuisance. Some of the moisture is removed by the chilling process referred to above, but enough would still remain to combine with the methane and form solid hydrates which might cause serious blockages in the pipeline and valves. To prevent this from happening, glycol (antifreeze) is injected as a spray before the gas passes into the expansion chamber.

PLATE 7. Three types of low-pressure gas holders in common use. *Top to bottom:* External frame water-sealed, spirally-guided water-sealed, and MAN waterless.

(By courtesy of Clayton, Son & Co. Ltd.)

PLATE 8. A group of cylindrical high-pressure gas holders in Kent.

(*By courtesy of Whessoe Ltd.*)

The glycol attracts the water, and the two together form a lower layer in the hydrocarbon condensate which is drawn off as it collects. The glycol is recovered from the solution by distilling off the water and can be used again.

L.P. GASES

Although methane is the largest constituent of natural gas, it is not the only important part. Half way between gas and liquid come the liquefiable petroleum gases such as propane and butane which occur both in natural gas and in petroleum. Intermediate in properties between methane and petrol, they have the great advantage of easy storage. They have boiling points (at ordinary atmospheric pressure) of −42°C and 0°C respectively, but they can be made to stay liquid at ordinary room temperatures by confining them in a relatively light metal container under pressure.

The following table summarizes the properties of these gases. (We neglect, for the moment, other constituents such as *iso*-butane, propylene, butylene, which occur in L.P. gas from refineries, and are in any case not widely different in their properties.)

TABLE I

	Methane CH_4	Propane C_3H_8	Butane C_4H_{10}
Boiling Point (at atmospheric pressure) °C	−161·5	−42	−0·5
Vapour pressure at 21°C (70°F)			
lb/sq. in (abs)	—	124·3	31·3
atmospheres abs	—	8·5	2·1
Density of gas (air 1·0)	0·55	1·55	2·08
Limits of inflammability in air (%)	5 to 15	2·4 to 9·5	1·8 to 8·4
Volume of air required for combustion	9·6	23·9	31·1
Maximum flame velocity cm/s.	66	81	84
Calorific value: in Btu/cu. ft	1,012	2,563	3,390
in Kcal/cu. m	9,150	23,200	30,600

The L.P. gases are important to the gas industry in two ways. In the first place, they provide a portable source of gas supply, and as such are most useful to caravan dwellers, campers, and people living in remote areas away from towns' gas supplies. However, these substances are gaining more and more importance as raw materials for gas manufacture. The fact that they can be stored relatively simply, but give rise on demand to a high-calorific-value gas, makes them extremely useful in the modern gasworks.

They can also be carried in ocean-going tankers, in a similar manner to methane; the problems are much less with L.P. gas, because the temperatures are not nearly so low. In Great Britain, this liquid is imported from the U.S.A. and landed at Felixstowe, whence a pipeline takes it to a new gasworks at Norwich. Here it is 're-formed' into town gas.

METHANE FROM OTHER NATURAL SOURCES

By far the most important source of commercial methane is from the earth, either associated with petroleum or occurring separately. Another, related, source has already been mentioned: that associated with coal. This is really a most interesting story, for ever since men began to go deep into the earth for coal, methane or 'firedamp' has been a source of great danger.

In the case of coal, the mechanism of gas formation is clearer. There is no doubt that methane was one of the products formed in the 'coalification' reaction by which the original forest debris was modified and turned to coal. In the case of broken seams or those lying near the surface, this methane will often have escaped, and miners speak of 'gassy pits' and 'non-gassy pits'. Most coal mines have to contend with a certain amount of methane, however, and this is normally liberated as the coal is hewn from the seam. The faster the coal face moves back, the more gas will be liberated; at one time the rate of production of some mines was controlled by the amount of methane which could be permitted in the air.

Mining engineers have evolved very thorough methods of ventilating every corner of the mine by a continuous current of air blown in by big fans. In spite of the very large volume blown through, it is quite common for the air which passes out to contain 1 per cent of methane; many mines blow as much as a million cubic feet of methane into the atmosphere in this manner every day.

In the years which have passed since the end of the Second World War, great strides have been made in 'draining' this methane from the rocks *before* it can contaminate the atmosphere of the mine. Since methane is lighter than air, these 'drains' go upwards, not downwards. They are, in fact, holes drilled up into the rocks which lie above the coal for a distance of perhaps 100 feet. When first drilled they do not yield much gas, but as the coal is removed from under them the whole rock structure is fissured and the trapped gas is able to escape, to be sucked away along tubes which run

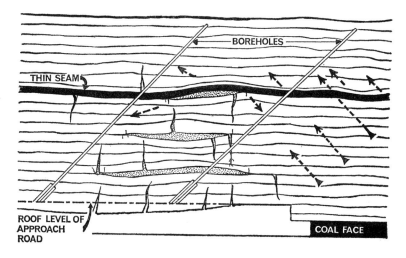

Fig. 10. Diagrammatic section of a coal-mine showing how the methane gas is liberated from the strata overlying the coal measure. The boreholes are made from the approach roads, the roofs of which are, of course, shored up. In the space between the approach roads the roof is allowed to sink.

along the underground passages, and often are prolonged to the surface.

Not only does this technique make the mine a far safer place to work in—and, incidentally, reduce the time lost through stoppages which might otherwise have been caused by a high methane concentration—but it also provides a free source of fuel gas at the pithead. This is a game in which you do not have to rob Peter to pay Paul: they both get paid!

The firedamp so extracted consists, as a rule, of perhaps 60 per cent methane—the rest being air and a little carbon dioxide. It is not a particularly convenient gas for the gas undertaking, although in small quantities it can be added to coal gas without causing any difficulty. Probably the best use of firedamp is in the firing of coke ovens, and this technique was pioneered in the Saar district when under French rule after the end of the Second World War. Much more recently it has been put into operation in Britain; in particular, the very large coke oven works at Wath-on-Dearne, near Doncaster, is supplied by six or seven coal mines which have been linked up to the town by pipelines.

METHANE FROM SEWAGE

The methane which comes from the bacterial decomposition of organic matter is as 'natural' a gas as one could imagine, though as a matter of convenience we reserve the term 'natural gas' for gas extracted from the rocks. However, methane is sometimes known as marsh gas and is formed in stagnant ponds from rotting vegetation. 'The will-o'-the-wisp' is said to be burning marsh gas.

However this may be, quite large quantities of methane mixed with carbon dioxide are formed in modern methods of sewage treatment. Several types of small-scale plant have also been designed for the production of methane from farm waste by fermentation. In each case there are two stages: first, fermentation under aerated conditions, during which air is blown through the liquid suspension. After this comes fermentation of the solid residue under anaerobic conditions—that is to say, with oxygen excluded. At this stage it is helpful to provide some heat to increase the rate of fermentation, and of course the right kind of bacteria must be present. The process is continued for a week or two, and during this time methane mixed with carbon dioxide is evolved.

The total amount of 'sludge gas' obtained in this manner is considerable. The sewage works serving the Greater London area, for instance, together produce about 6 million cubic feet of gas per day —enough to supply a city the size of Bradford. Unfortunately, no great enthusiasm has been shown in the integration of such supplies into the national resources. In most cases the gas is used only to provide power for the works themselves.

OTHER SOURCES OF GAS

Rather doubtfully within the scope of this chapter, but nevertheless of great importance, is the supply of gases obtained from oil refineries—known as refinery gas or (sometimes) tail gas. The modern oil refinery is really much more than its name implies. It long ago ceased to be content simply to separate out, or refine, oil; nowadays its function is to manufacture the desired products out of the raw materials available.

As we have already mentioned, the changing pattern of civilized life calls for varying proportions of the different petroleum products. It is the business of the oil refinery to supply these as efficiently as possible, but inevitably a considerable quantity of gaseous products are formed in the process which cannot easily be re-synthesized into oils.

The most economical way of using these gases is to sell them to the gas undertaking, which will then have the job of converting them to a form suitable for supplying to customers. The strip of heavily populated coastlands in Holland which includes Rotterdam and Amsterdam was until recently supplied almost entirely from the giant oil refineries of Pernis, near Amsterdam. In East London the Romford works is adapted to treat the hydrocarbon gases coming from the refineries lying along the north bank of the Thames estuary; on the south side, the Isle of Grain works performs a similar function.

Another industrial product which must be mentioned in passing is blast furnace gas. Wherever iron is smelted, blast furnaces are used. In them iron ore and coke react together to liberate the elementary iron. This takes place at a high temperature, and in consequence the gases which leave the top of a blast furnace contain a large amount of carbon monoxide together with nitrogen and some carbon dioxide.

Blast furnace gas is therefore a very low-grade gas, having a calorific value of perhaps 100 Btu/cu. ft. It is quite a valuable fuel so long as it can be used close at hand—the cost of transporting it for long distances would be quite prohibitive. It is normally used on the industrial site where it is generated, and rarely does it pass outside.

This chapter began with a consideration of the mineral fuels stored in the earth's crust. We have ended with reference to one or

D

two gases which—although they originate from there in the first place—occur as by-products in manufacturing industries. Taking them together with the manufactured gases described in Chapter 2, we have now covered the whole gamut of fuel gases which are (or could be) produced on a commercial scale. Most of the remainder of this book deals with the ways in which this gas is distributed, stored, and utilized.

4 | Gas Storage and Distribution

Most commodities, such as gas, water, or electricity, are used more at some times of the day than at others, and more at some seasons than at others. It is therefore important to be able to store when demand is small so that supplies can be augmented when demand is big. In this respect gas is very fortunate, and electricity is unlucky. An electricity generating station must make electric current at the very moment it is demanded. The size of its generators depends on the maximum output, even though that maximum may only last for 5 minutes in 24 hours.

By contrast, the classical gas-making stations were able to operate at a uniform speed, producing gas at a constant rate all round the clock—because they could store it till needed. The gas industry might have perished under competition from its electrical rival if it were not for this enormous advantage it enjoys. Even if gas is not made locally but is supplied from a distance, storage is still an important consideration. The pipeline is able to run at full capacity day and night if there is adequate storage capacity at the receiving end.

WATER-SEALED STORAGE HOLDERS

Much the oldest type of gas holder, and one still giving good service today, is the water-sealed holder. In basic principle this is a tumbler inverted in a bowl of water. You first ensure that the glass is full of water, invert it without letting in any air, and then bubble your gas up inside. If the tumbler is not to capsize it will have to be anchored to some system of guides so that it can move freely up and down but cannot topple over.

This kind of gas holder has the useful property of exerting an almost constant pressure on the gas inside. We say "almost", because the glass weighs rather less (on account of buoyancy) when it is low down in the water than when it rides high. The pressure can be varied by altering the weight on top of the bell, but of course this cannot be carried too far or the gas will begin to bubble out round the edge.

Another useful property of the water-sealed holder is that it gives an immediate and obvious visual display of the quantity of gas contained at any moment. Old gasworks employees will reckon the

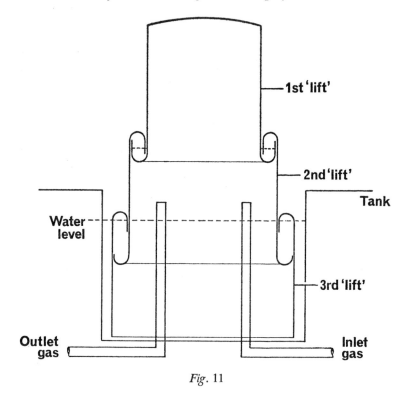

Fig. 11

amount of gas in a holder by the number of 'plates' visible—i.e., the plates of steel from which the outer shell has been fabricated. It was this habit that led to the old name, 'gasometer', which was used very widely by the public until a few years ago.

Of course, the use of a simple non-articulated bell would necessitate the use of an enormous water tank if it were applied in practice. To obviate this, it is usual to make the bell in several sections or 'lifts' (see Fig. 11) which telescope inside one another as the bell falls and the holder empties. To ensure that gas does not leak at the joints between these sections, the upper edge of the outer section is made to curl over and fit into a channel running round the lower edge of the section which fits inside it. This channel naturally carries up some of the water from the tank when it rises, and the water seal thus provided keeps the holder gastight.

Either the holder rides in water contained in a well dug out of the earth, or else in a tank constructed from steel sheets to stand above ground level. In any case the incoming gas enters by a pipe passing under the lowest position of the edge of the bell, and ending, above the level of the water, inside the bell. A similar pipe is used to remove the gas; often gas is flowing into the holder and out of it at the same time; it then serves as a mixing device to make the product more uniform.

A conspicuous feature of the older gas holders was the structural framework of girders (often adorned with nineteenth century ornamentation) which carried the guide rails. These vertical rails engaged grooved pulleys fixed on the top of each section, so preventing any possibility of tilting. More recent holders obviate the need for such a structure by employing the spirally guided principle.

In a spirally guided holder there are still rails, but they take the shape of a helix fixed to the outside of each section; they engage with grooved wheels at the top of the section which slides outside it. When the holder is first filled the innermost section begins to rise, rotating as it does so, because its rails are engaging with the wheels on the top of the next section (which at this stage is still resting on the tank bottom). See Plate 7.

When the innermost (i.e. the top) section is fully filled, it begins to raise the next section, and this is guided in turn by the wheels at the top of the third section; so the process goes on until all the sections have lifted and the holder is full.

The spirally guided holder is more economical in construction than the externally guided type, but not many water-sealed gas holders of either pattern are being constructed today. They have some serious disabilities: (*a*) they are very costly to construct; (*b*) they are unsightly; (*c*) they are unsuitable for high pressures; (*d*) they are vulnerable to frost unless special precautions are taken. As regards appearance, great trouble has been taken by some authorities to reduce the unsightliness of these holders by careful colour treatment of the bell, but as the painted metal is continually being immersed and re-immersed in the water of the tank it is very difficult to maintain an elegant appearance for long.

DRY LOW-PRESSURE HOLDERS

In an effort to overcome some of the disadvantages listed above, several patterns of gas holder have been evolved which are not water-sealed. In place of the container floating on water, expanding and contracting as it fills and empties, we have a fixed shell and a piston or floor moving up and down inside the shell, the gas being confined below the piston. The obvious problem to be faced by the engineer in designing such a system is: how to prevent gas escaping round the sides of the piston?

There have been two practical answers to this problem. The first was introduced in Germany in the 1930s and is known as the M.A.N. waterless holder; it has been used in Britain and elsewhere to a considerable extent. In this system the inside of the shell is polygonal rather than circular, and each facet of the piston carries a canvas curtain which is kept wet with a stream of tar being pumped over it continuously. The pressure of the gas pushes the canvas curtain on to the walls of the containing shell, and so gas leakage is virtually eliminated.

This type of holder was (surprisingly perhaps) cheaper to build than the water-sealed holder. Although it remained the same size whether full or empty, it proved in practice to be rather pleasanter in appearance because the shell could be maintained in good condition with regular painting. However, the use of this holder introduced an element of danger which was entirely missing in the water-sealed type.

Flame and explosion (see Chapter 8) is possible only when gas and air are mixed together in proportions which lie between the limits of inflammability—with ordinary town gas about 6 to 35 per cent gas in air. If the shell of a water-sealed holder is punctured gas will rush out, and may burn in a giant torch, but the holder itself cannot possibly explode.

In a waterless holder, however, we have a shell containing both gas (below the piston) and air (above it), so there is the theoretical possibility of a very big explosion if the two should mix and become ignited. One of the very first holders of this type, at Neunkirchen, in the Saar Territory, actually exploded in the years before the Second World War and caused great havoc. When war broke out in 1939 all such holders in Britain were immediately emptied and were not used again until after the war was over. So far as the author is aware, no serious accident has taken place since the Neunkirchen disaster, and ample precautions are taken by the authorities operating holders of this type today. For instance, if the piston departs from the exact horizontal position an immediate alarm is sounded so that steps can be taken to rectify the fault without delay.

Another type of waterless gasholder, much more recent in design, is the Wiggins. This uses a continuous fold of fabric to connect the piston to the outer shell. The fabric is made of synthetic rubber-coated material. A small gasholder of this type is situated at the Canvey Island methane reception station (see Chapter 5) for the storage of gas which has boiled off from the liquefied gas.

HIGH-PRESSURE HOLDERS

The low-pressure gas holders we have just been describing were developed in the age of the small gasworks. Such a works might only supply the district for a radius of a few miles around, and distribution was by cast iron pipes, operating at a pressure of perhaps 5 inches or 6 inches water column.* Usually there would be no connection with any other gasworks, and the reliability of the supply to the area would depend entirely upon the continuous operation of the local works. This works would make gas at a uniform rate of production throughout the 24 hours, and the gas holders would dispense the gas so made to the customers as required.

This kind of undertaking still exists, but it is becoming increasingly uncommon as more and more of the small units are linked up by national or regional pipeline systems. With this integration comes the use of distribution at much higher pressures—50 (or even 70) atmospheres can be used in long distance pipelines.

When such pressures are available, the most economical way of storing gas at the end of the supply line is to put it at pressure into specially constructed tanks. These commonly take the form of horizontal cylinders, with domed ends. They have no moving parts

---

[1] For a note on units of pressure see page 55. Four inches of water is equivalent to about one hundredth of an atmosphere.

at all; the gas is compressed into them and is taken out by simple expansion.

One obvious advantage of such an installation (see Plate 8) is that its appearance is far more acceptable. Whereas a water-sealed holder containing the same amount of gas might be a landmark for miles around, this installation of pressure cylinders will only occupy about one fiftieth of the volume (if the gas is compressed to 50 atmospheres pressure), and can soon be concealed by a screen of fast-growing trees.

Great care is necessary in constructing such vessels. The welds must all be examined by one of the techniques described later in this chapter, and before use the vessel is tested with water to a pressure considerably above the maximum at which it will be used. It must be examined at intervals to make sure that the initial strength is maintained and has not been weakened by corrosion. Attention is also given to providing for thermal expansion, and the cradles on which it is mounted will normally be provided with rollers to allow slight movement.

The gas pipes themselves which carry gas over long distances at high pressures, hold a considerable reserve of gas, and one ingenious way of making a high-pressure storage system is deliberately to lay larger-diameter pipes than are strictly necessary for the carrying of the gas. Large-diameter pipes are, naturally, dearer to buy and dearer to lay; but the net increase is considerably less than it would cost to construct a special holder station.

The gas usually leaves a high pressure holder through a pressure governor. This is a valve controlled by the outlet pressure; if it falls the valve opens a little more to restore it. A rise in the outlet pressure closes the valve (see end of this chapter). Using a system of this kind, the gas can be fed into the local mains as required.

UNITS OF PRESSURE

Gas engineers use a number of different units to describe pressure. They use inches (or centimetres) of water for the lowest pressures, inches (or centimetres) of mercury, lb/sq. in or kg/sq. cm, and finally atmospheres (or bars) for the highest pressures of all.

The gas supply reaches the ordinary household in a town at a relatively small pressure; that is to say, the difference between the pressure inside the pipe and that of the atmosphere outside it would only support a few inches of water column. If the engineer connects a pressure gauge (Fig. 12) to one of these pipes, the liquid inside it is forced up a certain distance and this is expressed in 'inches water gauge'—probably 5 or 6 inches for the ordinary domestic supply.

Industrial users of gas often require a higher pressure than this. They find it convenient to use a much denser liquid, mercury, in

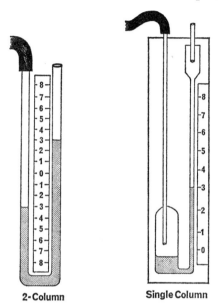

2-Column   Single Column

Fig. 12. Two types of pressure gauge. In the single-column type it is only necessary to read the position of one liquid level.

their gauges. This has a density of 13·6 times that of water, so 13·6 inches water gauge is the equivalent of 1 inch of mercury. For higher pressures still, use is made of a mechanical movement rather like that of an aneroid barometer; the expansion of a metal diaphragm causes a needle to move over a dial. At this stage the engineer begins to use lb/sq. in or kg/sq. cm. He may also speak of atmospheres because, when the difference between the inside and the outside of a container is 30 inches mercury (or 14·7 lb/sq. in) the gas inside is subjected to twice the normal atmospheric pressure.[1]

[1] The Germans have an excellent system of describing pressure in atmospheres: they use "atü" for atmospheres above normal atmospheric pressure, and "ata" for atmospheres absolute. In English we have no such convenient system.

The following table shows the relationships between the main pressure units:

13·6 inches water gauge = 1 inch mercury

about 400 inches water gauge = 30 inches mercury = 1 atmosphere

$$\left.\begin{array}{l} 14\cdot 7 \text{ lb/sq. in (or p.s.i.)} \\ 1 \text{ kg/sq. cm} \end{array}\right\} = 1 \text{ atmosphere}$$

In this book we are trying to keep things as simple as possible. We therefore use only two units: the inch water gauge (w.g.), and the atmosphere.

UNDERGROUND STORAGE IN AQUIFERS

One of the most astonishing developments in recent history has been the use of geological strata for the storing of large amounts of gas. This technique originated in the United States, where some of the gas fields near large centres of population became exhausted at quite an early stage. It was thought that the exhausted rocks could be made to serve as reservoirs by pumping gas back into them through the old well holes.

The scheme worked exceedingly well, and for the first time gas storage was able to cover, not merely the variation in demand from hour to hour during the day, but the variation from season to season during the year. This meant that the pipelines bringing gas from far away could be operated at full load all the summer when demand for gas was small, because the gas could be temporarily pushed into the earth. Then, in winter time, when all the central heating plants were switched on, enough gas to meet all the requirements could be found by extracting gas that had been pushed underground during the summer.

The European gas engineers heard of this remarkable achievement, and wanted to emulate it. However, in Western Europe there were practically no gas fields at that time, and certainly no conveniently situated exhausted gas fields.[1] Work was started on the first 'artificial' storage system at a small village called Engelbostel, seven miles from Hanover, in 1951; the actual injection of gas into the rock strata began in 1954, and it has been in use ever since.

---

[1] In 1955 an almost exhausted gas field in South Poland was adapted for use as a gas reservoir.

This was quite a remarkable achievement. The American gas engineers had been able to use their old gas fields with some confidence that they were gas tight. Had they not held gas for millions of years before the field was tapped? But to construct a storage zone (now generally known as an 'aquifer') in strata which had not before held gas required much more caution. The engineers had to ask themselves: would it be gas-tight, or would their precious fuel gas come bubbling up in some other place where it would be most unwelcome and perhaps dangerous?

It was also necessary to consider that an amount of gas equivalent to a large sum of money must be injected in order to start the aquifer going. Would the results justify such an expenditure? And, finally, would the injection of the gas cause any fouling of the water supplies drawn from the earth by artesian wells?

As things turned out, the site at Engelbostel had been well chosen. Many careful tests were made before it was decided that the project could go ahead quite safely. Coke oven gas (the surplus during the summer months) was then injected into the porous sandstone layers 700 feet below the surface, at a pressure of 40 atmospheres. The gas made its way into the pores of the sandstone, driving out the salt water which formerly saturated it.

Geological surveys had already established that above the sandstone lay a reasonably thick and impervious layer of clay. The pattern in which the strata lie at this place is such that they form a dome or anticline which can trap the gas. The degree of porosity of the sandstone was known; this controls the amount of gas which can be stored in a given volume of rock. A property which is related, but not identical, is the permeability. This affords a measure of the ease with which a gas can be pushed *through* a sandstone layer; it depends on the extent to which the pores are interconnected.

Fig. 13 is based on the Engelbostel installation. Here are two boreholes, both of which are in section; in practice there would be more boreholes than this. The centre holes would be used to inject gas during input periods and also to remove gas during withdrawal. A borehole off the diagram to the right would be used purely for test purposes; it would record the pressure in the brine layer, and would probably be arranged to sound an alarm if the gas should ever reach it.

Another hole (not shown) would be a further test point; located at the edge of the reservoir, and indicating the extent to which the gas 'bubble' is spread out. From the well-heads gathering pipes run to the central purification installations and compressor station. The gas must normally be compressed to drive it into the aquifer, and this compression heats the gas; the heat must be removed before it is

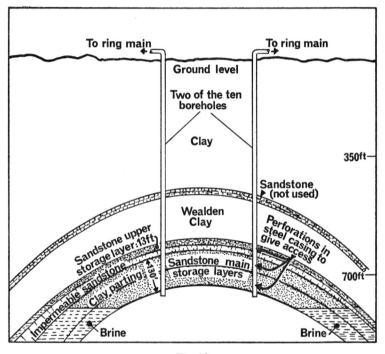

Fig. 13

injected into the ground. When it is coal gas whicn is being stored (as at Engelbostel), additional precautions are taken to remove minute traces of organic substances which might cause gummy deposits to form round the base of each borehole and reduce the permeability of the sandstone. The gas which is withdrawn from the aquifer must also be purified to remove exceedingly small quantities of iron and nickel carbonyl which can be formed by contact with the rocks at this high pressure, and which are very troublesome indeed if allowed to travel in the gas supplied to the public. Usually the gas must be dried also; for it is of course saturated with water vapour when extracted (it may even contain salt spray).

Since the aquifer at Engelbostel was established, at least five others have been set up in Europe, some for coal gas and others for either natural gas or (as at Hamburg) refinery gas. In Britain a serious attempt was made to get official approval for a scheme at Chilcomb Down, near Winchester. Here the strata are similar to the formation at Beynes, near Versailles, where a large aquifer is in use, storing the coal gas which supplies Paris. Local opposition, some of it very ill-informed, succeeded in preventing the Gas Council from securing the changes in the law which they judged to be necessary if the Chilcomb Down project was to be realized.

The ordinary systems of land ownership give to the proprietor of the surface rights over all the ground beneath his feet. The mediaeval jurists did not, of course, conceive that one day it might be desirable, in the interests of the community, to be able to establish a gas 'pool' in the rocks 500 feet below the soles of the landowner's feet—a gas pool which could have no conceivable effect on the use of the land at or near the surface.

The British Parliament has accordingly taken steps, in the 1965 Gas Act, to establish the responsibility of a gas authority, under the instructions of the Minister of Power, for all underground storage systems. Britain certainly needs underground storage very acutely, and the need will become even more urgent if natural gas is brought from Holland or from the North Sea by pipeline (or by tanker). If this happens, the full advantages will not be realized unless it is possible to bring the gas into the country at a uniform rate, storing it during summer for use in the winter.

GAS DISTRIBUTION

Just as electricity is distributed by wires, so gas is distributed by pipes. Although the two processes are in reality very different, there is also a rough parallel between the concept of gas pressure and electric voltage; on this analogy, electric current would correspond to gas volume rate of flow. The comparison soon breaks down if one carries it much further, but it is worth noticing a further parallel: just as, by employing a higher voltage, one can use thinner conducting wires, so the use of higher gas pressures enables smaller-bore pipes to be employed.

In an electric conductor the drop in voltage between any two points is directly proportional to the current flowing, but gas is not quite so obliging. In a pipe the 'voltage drop' is proportional to *the square* of the rate of flow. Thus while a 2-volt drop would become 4 volts if the current were doubled, a pressure difference of 4 inches (water gauge) becomes 16 inches if twice the amount of gas flows.

This is true for the kind of flow which occurs in most long-distance gas pipes, but in reality there are two patterns of flow, streamline (or laminar) and turbulent. Streamline flow takes places at low velocities,

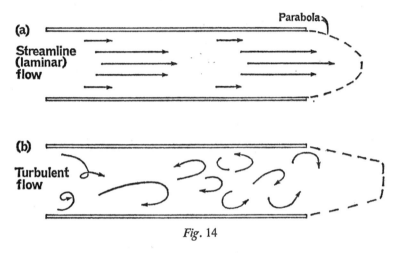

Fig. 14

and especially in narrow channels; each layer then moves parallel to the next, so that the fluid closest to the pipe wall is quite still. The speed is fastest in the middle, and if you plot the speed of the fluid against the distance across the diameter, the curve obtained is a parabola (Fig. 14 (*a*)). This ideal state of affairs is soon disturbed if the velocity is increased beyond a critical value. Then the turning moment caused by one layer rubbing against the next can no longer be resisted—eddies begin to develop, and before long the smooth flow pattern has been completely broken up.

Fig. 14 (*b*) gives an idea of what turbulent flow would look like if you could see it. No longer does the gas move in straight lines parallel to the walls, but a complicated random pattern of eddies swirls along, continually changing. The flow immediately adjacent to the walls is still slower than the rest, but for the rest of the cross-section the flow is at approximately uniform velocity; the distribution is now square-headed rather than parabolic.

The critical velocity at which streamline flow breaks down and turbulent flow takes its place depends upon a number of factors; in particular, on the density of the fluid, the diameter of the pipe, and the viscosity of the fluid.[1] One can combine these factors together as follows:

$$\frac{\text{velocity} \times \text{density} \times \text{diameter}}{\text{viscosity}} = Re$$

Re stands for the Reynolds Number, named after Osborne Reynolds. In a long straight pipe, flow is streamline so long as *Re* lies below about 2000[2]. Then, if you increase either velocity, density, or diameter of pipe, the flow will change and become turbulent; unless, of course, you intervene to redress the balance by increasing the viscosity.

With viscous liquids (such as crude petroleum) streamline flow is quite likely to occur, but gas is of course much less viscous and streamline flow rarely occurs in practical gas distribution systems unless they are working far below the load for which they were designed.

LONG-DISTANCE PIPELINES

A pipeline can stretch for 2000 miles or more, and may carry gas at a pressure of 60 or even 100 atmospheres. A given volume of gas can be transported in either a large pipe at relatively low pressure, which involves relatively thin walls and low pumping costs, or at a

[1] We are all familiar with viscosity in liquids; engine oil is more viscous than water, for instance. Viscosity is really an internal friction resisting the movement of one part over another; it therefore slows down the rate of passage through an orifice, or the rate at which you can pour a liquid. It is expressed as a force per unit area; the tangential force needed to drag one area of liquid over another. Gases are very much less viscous than liquids, of course, but they still have a viscosity which can be measured and which affects their behaviour when flowing in pipes. Hydrogen is the least viscous of common gases, and oxygen has a viscosity more than twice as great.

[2] A simple number is given, without any units (feet, grammes, etc.) because *Re* is dimensionless; if your velocity, density, diameter, and viscosity are all in the metric system or all in feet, pounds, and seconds, the result will be the same. *Re* is a pure number.

higher pressure by using thicker (or at least stronger) walls and facing higher pumping costs. The economist decides the size of pipe to be laid after weighing all these factors, and taking into account also the possible future demands on the pipeline.

The building of such a pipeline is quite an exciting piece of organization. Several hundred men will probably be engaged upon it; collectively they are termed a 'spread'. They are indeed spread out—the distance between the vanguard and the rearguard may be 5 or even 10 miles. The men in front will be clearing the ground of bushes, trees, fences, etc., and where necessary fencing off the strip to prevent cattle straying on to it.

Behind this group may come a ditching machine, which ploughs its way along, leaving a trench some 4 to 6 feet deep and perhaps 3 feet wide. It piles up the soil by the side of the trench in a neat ridge; on agricultural land it will traverse the ground twice, piling top soil to one side and deep soil on the other. This is necessary to keep the ground fertile; after the pipe has been laid the deep soil will be thrown in first and the top soil after it.

A short distance behind, lorries will be bringing up lengths of pipe and placing them carefully on the ground so that they are just the right distance apart, along the side of the trench. After them come some very important men, the welders; they join one length to the next by a film of molten steel. Usually at least three sets of welders are used, one behind the other, to fill up the groove where the pipe ends have been joined until it is level with the pipe surface.

Welding is a highly skilled operation, and one which is vital to the success of the whole enterprise. A bad welder can leave blowholes or particles of slag in the weld, and so make it much weaker than it should be. Not only are the welders trained very carefully, but their work is inspected by X-ray machines (or gamma rays from radio-isotopes) or sometimes by ultrasonic sound waves. All these methods will show up a fault in the weld, even though from the surface it may appear perfect.

Behind the welders come the weld testers, therefore; and behind them come the weld wrappers, who must cover the weld with a protective coating—usually made up of pitch, glass fibre, and asbestos. This is the case when the pipe is delivered already wrapped to the site; but sometimes bare pipe is delivered, and then the whole pipe, welds and all, is wrapped by a gigantic machine which sends

PLATE 9. A ditching machine, which digs the trench in which the pipe-line is laid.

PLATE 10. A pipeline coating and wrapping machine working on a section of the line on Salisbury Plain. The seamless piping is first coated with hot bitumen and then wrapped with fibreglass as a protection against corrosion.

(*An Esso Photograph*)

four huge cotton-reels spinning round the pipe. Each reel carries a band of glass fibre or asbestos cloth and the machine pours hot molten pitch on to the pipe at the same time.

Behind the pipe protectors comes the small group who test the wrapping for gaps or pinholes—which might allow the ingress of water and start corrosion after the pipe has been buried. Another group of men will be preparing the bottom of the trench to see that any sharp stones are removed—they might cut into the coating if they were not taken away. Usually a layer of sand or magnesite is laid along the bottom of the trench.

Then comes another rather spectacular procedure: the pipe, now lying complete along the side of the trench, must be picked up and 'snaked-in' to its final resting place. When this has been done, the earth is shovelled back into the trench by a bulldozer and nothing remains but a muddy strip of earth above the pipe. Even this soon disappears, and a year later grass or corn or other crops may be growing here and you would need a map to tell where the pipeline is buried.

Such a 'spread' will work steadily, progressing a mile a day or sometimes even faster. It requires a most carefully worked out control, for obviously the slow or imperfect operation of just one of these separate gangs could slow up the whole rate of progress.

Once the pipe has been laid, tested, and brought into service, it performs its work quietly and unseen for many years to come. Of course, pipelines laid in uninhabited desert need not necessarily be placed underground; but even if they are left lying on the surface, their construction is a very considerable engineering task. Such pipes are those bringing oil from the Iraq oilfields across to the Mediterranean, while another large pipe takes gas from Bokhara and conveys it along the shores of the Aral Sea to Cheliabinsk, 1300 miles to the north. (See Chapter 7.)

PIPELINES IN TOWNS

Rather less sensational, but no less important, are the pipes (or mains) which distribute gas in town and city. Under almost every roadway (or better under the pavement) lie a number of cables and pipes—so many, indeed, that the construction of a new road tunnel necessitates a great deal of preliminary work in re-routing the gas, water, electricity, and sewage conduits.

E

The gas pipes under town streets are usually made of cast iron, and often have no protection on the outside. Cast iron cannot easily be welded, and therefore the lengths are joined together by one of several types of mechanical joint. By far the commonest type is the spigot-and-socket; one end of the pipe is belled out so that the plain end of the next length can be pushed into it. The space in between is filled (in the older pipes) with hemp and tallow, followed by a strip of lead which has been run into the joint.

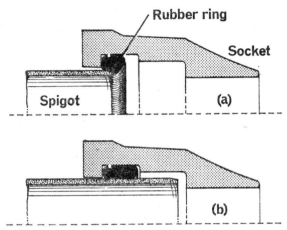

Fig. 15. One method of joining pipes. The rubber ring, shown in position at (*a*), is squeezed between two surfaces when the joint is pushed together (*b*).

More modern joints incorporate rings made of a special oil-resistant rubber—one typical example is shown in Fig. 15. This has the advantage that it permits slight angular movement without the danger of leaks being caused thereby. The pressure in these pipes is very much lower than that used in the long-distance pipeline; 7 or 8 inches of water column (say, 1/50 atmosphere) is usual. There may also be medium-pressure mains which distribute gas to the low-pressure main; these may function at 30 or even 40 inches pressure.

From the low-pressure main, branches are taken off to supply the individual premises; these are always known as service pipes.

While steel is the traditional material, service pipes are now often made of one of the plastics—usually PVC (polyvinyl chloride). This material has the great advantage of freedom from soil corrosion, and its lightness makes it far easier to transport and install. Some doubts as to the effects of benzene on the material have delayed full acceptance, but it now seems fairly clear that rigid PVC is quite satisfactory in use from this point of view, even with coal gas.

INSIDE THE HOUSE

The pipe system is carried on inside the house, passing through the gas meter (see Chapter 12), but at this stage it is always in metal pipe; plastic is not generally acceptable because it would melt if a fire were to break out. The pipes inside a building are usually a part of the house structure; they belong to the owner of the house or

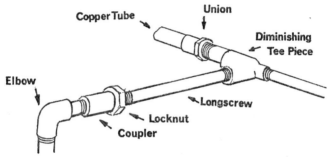

Fig. 16. Examples of connections used in joining gas pipes. The units are mostly of steel; the union enables copper tubing to be connected to steel.

factory. The supply system up to and including the meter usually belongs to the gas supply undertaking.

Inside a house the pipes are usually joined together by screwed connections. A screw thread is cut on the end of each length of pipe, and a coupler (threaded internally) serves to connect the two ends together. If a branch is needed at this point, a tee-piece is used (Fig. 16). However, there are some places where a simple screwed joint is not practicable, for the tubing cannot be twisted—for instance, with connections to a gas cooker or a gas fire. Obviously it is not feasible to twist the whole gas cooker when connecting it to the gas supply.

There are two devices commonly used to solve this problem: the longscrew and the union (see Fig. 16). Both enable two pipes to be united in a gas-tight joint without any twisting of the pipes.

GOVERNORS

It remains to mention a very useful device which is widely used in gas supply; this is the pressure governor. A simple form of this device is shown in Fig. 17. It consists essentially of a valve formed by a plunger A and a seating B. This valve is closed by a high pressure in the outlet C, because pressure here exerts an upward thrust on the leather diaphragm D. As soon as the pressure on the outlet falls, however, D falls too, allowing the valve to open.

By this very simple arrangement one can control the pressure on the outlet to an almost constant value. In the diagram a weight is shown controlling the downward thrust of the diaphragm, but this

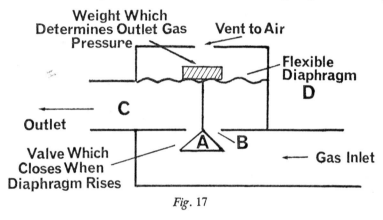

Fig. 17

weight can be replaced by a spring or by gas pressure from another source. When a weight load or a spring is used, ventilation holes are provided to keep the air above the diaphragm at atmospheric pressure. However, if these holes are omitted, and a small pipe is led into the upper chamber, gas pressure can be used; a high pressure gives the same effect as a large weight on the diaphragm.

This pressure-loading system proves very useful when really large volumes of gas are to be controlled, and especially if it is to be varied. For instance, one whole district may be supplied by a medium-pressure gas main. A governor is installed (usually in a pit underground) to control the pressure at which the gas flows into the low-pressure mains (which actually run through the streets to the houses). So long as the feeder mains pressure is higher than that in the low-pressure mains, the governor will give a constant outlet pressure.

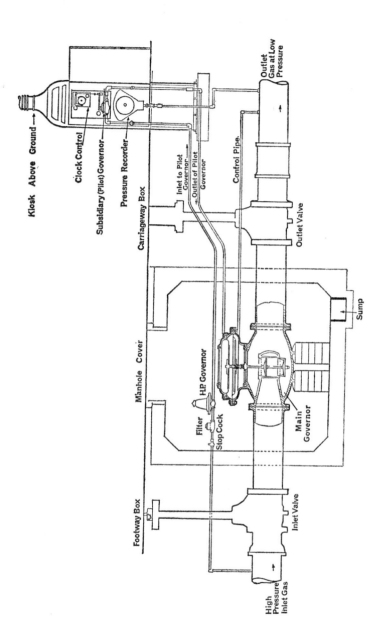

Klosk   Above   Ground →

Ciock Control

Subsidiary (Pilot) Governor

Pressure Recorder

Carriageway Box

Inlet to Pilot Governor

Outlet of Pilot Governor

Control Pipe.

Outlet Valve

Sump

H.P. Governor

Main Governor

Manhole   Cover

Filter

Stop Cock

Footway Box

Inlet Valve

High Pressure Inlet Gas

Outlet Gas at Low Pressure

Fig. 18. A district governor for controlling the pressure to an area of supply.

However, a constant pressure may not be what is really wanted. The rate at which the users want their gas varies greatly through the 24 hours, and it is usual to arrange that the district governor gives a higher outlet pressure at times when the demand is greatest. This is done by using the pressure-loading system. The pressure above the diaphragm in the main governor is varied by means of a clock controller fitted on a much smaller subsidiary governor. This works on gas which has been tapped off up-stream.

At 1 a.m., when most people are sleeping, the pressure in the gas main can be lowered to a value just high enough to keep essential services going. At 7.30 a.m. a great many people start to cook their breakfast, turn on their gas fire, and run hot water from their multipoint heater. The clock-controlled district governor will have anticipated this and increased the pressure so that all these demands can be met. Then, during the morning, it will probably be lowered again but will rise in time for the luncheon peak—and so on, throughout the day.

5 | Liquid Gas by Tanker

Until recently it seemed that the pipeline was the only practicable method of transporting gas. It still remains much the best method for short distances over land, or indeed over long distances provided that the points of supply and of delivery are firmly established, and can be relied upon to remain unchanged for a considerable time ahead.

The pipeline is, however, a rather inflexible mode of transport. A large capital sum is needed to deposit it in the earth, and once this has been done the pipe can be used only for this route and for no other. In cases where the supply point is in one country and the reception point is in another, this could mean that serious deterioration in the political relationship might put the pipe out of use; or the supplying country could possibly use the strength of its bargaining position to demand unreasonable increases in price.

Attention has therefore been given to the possibility of liquefying gas and conveying it by tanker. The hydrocarbon gases are all liquefiable (as indeed are all gases), but only those with three or more carbon atoms can be easily liquefied by pressure at room temperature.[1] The transport of L.P. gases by ship is relatively straightforward, and is already a well-established procedure. The conveyance of methane and ethane, however, is a new development and one which seems likely to become of great importance.

Methane must be maintained in a very cold condition if it is to remain liquid; above the critical temperature of $-82°C$ no amount of pressure will liquefy it. Usually it is more convenient to store it at pressures only just above atmospheric, and at temperatures which are near its boiling point $(-162°C)$. The storage of methane in liquid form therefore involves some quite fresh problems. It involves the use of materials for pipes, valves, tanks, etc., which will be

---

[1] Ethane can be kept as a liquid up to 32°C, but a pressure of 48 atmospheres is needed.

maintained at −162°C for long periods of time. At this temperature the physical properties of many substances are quite different from what they are at ordinary temperatures. Mild steel is brittle and weak; rubber tubing can be broken with a hammer.

It was a lack of proper appreciation of these difficulties which led to a terrible disaster in the United States in 1944. At Cleveland, Ohio, a large tank of conventional design was filled with liquid methane. Indeed, the design was in one respect unconventional in that no retaining wall seems to have been built around the tank to hold back the liquid if the tank should burst or leak. The mild steel of which the tank was made proved quite inadequate at this very low temperature, and the tank broke, discharging 100,000 gallons of liquid methane into the surrounding residential area. A fire broke out, with appalling loss of life.

FIRST EXPERIMENTS BY TANKER

This early demonstration of the dangers of liquid methane probably had the effect of discouraging other enterprises from experimenting for some time. However, in 1951 the Union Stockyard and Transit Co. of Chicago started to work on a scheme for carrying liquid methane in barges up the Mississippi and thence by the canal system to their stockyards in the city. It happened that the company owned a gas field in Louisiana, and liquefaction plant was to be installed nearby.

Apart from the economical carriage of fuel, an additional advantage was envisaged by the company—that the cold produced by the re-conversion of the methane liquid into gas at Chicago could be used to great advantage in the meat storage plant there. Just as heat is needed to turn water into steam when it boils, so heat is needed to vaporize liquid methane. The possibility of using such a cold substance to absorb heat in large quantities, and so act as a refrigerant, could be most valuable. Unfortunately it has not so far proved possible to use this idea in subsequent large-scale developments. (If the British gas authority could utilize it at Canvey Island to advantage it might reduce the cost of the gas by more than 10 per cent.)

The original Chicago scheme was not carried beyond the experimental stage, but the development work done by the Union Stockyard Co. showed that the carriage of liquid methane by tanker was a practical possibility. By 1956 both the Continental Oil Company and the Gas Council (of Britain) were closely interested, and work was started on the conversion of a 5000-ton cargo ship into a methane tanker, named the *Methane Pioneer*. This ship crossed the Atlantic in 1959 carrying gas which had been liquefied in Louisiana, and landed its cargo at a new terminal station which had been built on Canvey Island, on the north side of the Thames estuary.

SPECIAL DESIGN CONSIDERATIONS

This terminal station was specially constructed, and of course all possible precautions were taken to avoid any repetition of the 1944 disaster. The materials used were chosen to have good mechanical strength at these low temperatures. An alloy of aluminium was found to be suitable, but another metal which can be used is a nickel–steel alloy containing 9 per cent nickel.

In addition, very special attention must be given to the lagging (thermal insulation) of the tanks and of the pipes leading to and from them. It is not enough to apply a simple insulating material such as asbestos, and cover it with an outer casing to protect it mechanically. Unless special precautions are taken, moist air would soon diffuse into the insulation and deposit ice there. In a short time the insulation would be a solid block of ice and most of its thermal insulation (which is dependent essentially on the air spaces it contains) would be lost.

The outer casing over the insulation must therefore be, as near as possible, hermetically sealed. The insulating material inside it must be scrupulously dried before it is applied, and usually a current of a dry inert gas (such as nitrogen) is circulated through the lagging continuously. This maintains a small pressure in the space occupied by the insulating material, and ensures that if there is any leak it will be of dry gas *outwards* rather than of moist air *inwards*. These precautions apply to the tanks on board ship, the pipes running along the jetty, and the tanks on land.

Extreme precautions are taken to prevent any mixture of methane and air developing in an enclosed space, since a spark in such an atmosphere could set off a violent explosion. The way to prevent such an occurrence is in the first place to eliminate any chance of a spark or flame coming near, and in the second place to prevent the formation of an air–gas mixture.

The space above the liquid methane is always kept filled with methane gas. For instance, when the ship's tanks are being emptied into the shore storage system a second pipe is at the same time taking methane gas back to the ship to fill the space formerly taken up by the liquid. The gas is maintained at pressure, so that any leakage will be outwards rather than inwards.

The annular space around each tank (containing the thermal insulation) is kept filled with the inert gas nitrogen, under slight pressure. As it leaves the space, the nitrogen is passed through an analyser which will quickly record the presence of any methane. If the slightest leak in the inner lining should develop, it can therefore be detected very quickly, and action can be taken to reduce the possible danger.

Another aspect of the design which must be given careful consideration is the thermal expansion and contraction. The change in temperature of a metal such as aluminium from a normal ambient condition of perhaps 20°C down to −162°C or less causes quite a big alteration in the dimensions. In the case of aluminium, the metal will shrink by about 0·3 per cent. The pipes at Canvey Island run for 750 feet along a jetty; their length will change by 2 feet 6 inches, and the designer must make ample provision for this.

The tank lining will similarly shrink when the temperature is lowered, and this will be a shrinkage relative to the outer envelope (which must stay at approximately atmospheric temperature). Since the inner lining rests on a layer of insulation, the top of it will drop quite considerably; hence there must be a joint on the intake and output pipes which can expand and contract by a considerable amount (and of course remain absolutely gastight).

These contractions would impose great mechanical strains on the vessels unless the temperature were lowered gradually, and it follows that the process of putting them "on cold" must be done very carefully and slowly; otherwise grave distortion or even rupture might be caused. A certain amount of liquid methane is left in the bottom of the ship's tanks on the return journey, so that they remain in the cold condition all the while.

LIQUID METHANE IMPORTATION TO BRITAIN

From all these considerations (and many more) has emerged the grand scheme which is now supplying Britain with about 10 per cent of its total gas requirements. The twin ships, *Methane Princess* and *Methane Progress*, are plying between Canvey Island in the Thames and Arzew, on the coast of Algeria. At Arzew (near Oran) a large liquefaction plant (the first of its kind) receives gas piped from the gas fields of Hassi-er-R'Mel and converts it into liquid methane.

The Hassi-er-R'Mel gas fields lie in a stony desert area some 300 miles south of Arzew, 40 miles north of the oasis town of Ghardaia.

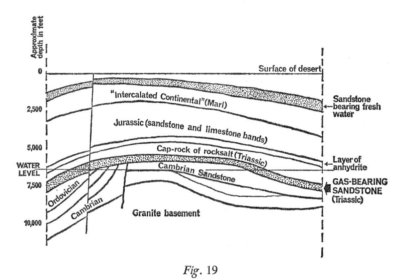

Fig. 19

The land is unpopulated (apart from the settlement operating the gas field) and almost devoid of vegetation. Yet 7000 feet below the surface lie three layers of porous sandstone which together have a thickness of about 200 feet—though each layer varies greatly in thickness from place to place. They are folded in an anticline (or elongated dome) which extends for 850 square miles; and there is gas in this vast reservoir at a pressure of 300 atmospheres and a temperature of 89°C. (See Fig. 19.)

While, it is true, the gas can only occupy the pore spaces in the rock, in this case these represent between 15 and 22 per cent of the total volume. A really vast quantity of gas is stored here—enough to supply Britain (at the present rate) for the next 1000 years! In the process of cooling the hot gas in the surface installations (by allowing it to expand suddenly) a liquid condensate consisting of valuable light oils is obtained, and this is piped off to an oilfield some eighty miles south. The gas still retains enough pressure (about 80 atmospheres) to enable it to run to Arzew without further pumping (though compressor stations will be needed along the route if the flow increases).

At Hassi-er-R'Mel (an Arabic name which means 'the sandy well') a new settlement has been built in the bare desert, and about 200 people live in two neat rows of single storey houses. Between them are rows of young trees, which have to be carefully tended and

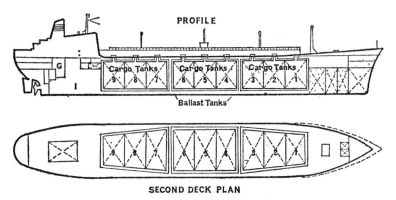

Fig. 20. The liquid methane is carried in tanks 1 to 9. Nitrogen is used as an inert gas to fill the insulation space round each group of tanks. The boiler room is at G, and the propulsive machinery at I.

fed with water pumped from underground strata. (The nearest decent-sized bush must be 40 miles away.) This colony maintains and operates the gas well-head plant, from which three giant stacks rear up into the sky, each of them crowned with a massive plume of red fire. This is the gas which is either surplus in amount or is at a low pressure and cannot easily be utilized. To the visitor it seems wasteful, but with so much wealth under their feet the oil men are not so sensitive.

The two methane tankers are both made to the same design. Each carries nine aluminium tanks with a total capacity of 12,200 tons. A cross-section is shown in Fig. 20. The tanks are insulated with panels of balsa wood supplemented by glass fibre. Balsa wood, so familiar to model aeroplane enthusiasts because of the combination of lightness and strength which characterizes it, has a fine cellular structure which makes it an excellent insulator. This wood lining has another function: if the aluminium lining should leak, it will retain the contents of the tank for at least another ten days (time to get it safely emptied).

The thermal insulation is important for several reasons. These ships carry no refrigeration plant to keep their cargo cold. They rely upon efficient insulation to prevent heat from getting in to the liquid. Of course, however good the insulation, a certain amount of heat will penetrate. This does not raise the temperature, but it causes a certain amount of boiling, and about 0·3 per cent of the total volume is lost each day. It is not lost completely, because the 'boil-off gas' is used to supplement the fuel oil used in the boiler room of the ship, and so provides some of the power for propulsion.

In normal operation the only metal parts which are at the temperature of liquid methane are the walls, floor, and ceiling of the tanks themselves. These are made of materials which have good mechanical properties at these low temperatures. The insulation therefore serves to protect any of the structural steelwork on the ship from the intense cold which would weaken it. As these ships are travelling back and forth across the Bay of Biscay they will normally be exposed to the stresses caused by stormy weather, and the very highest engineering standards are obviously called for.

ECONOMICS OF LIQUID METHANE TRANSPORTATION

The transport of natural gas in the form of a liquid is quite an expensive undertaking. It would be made a better economic proposition if some of the energy expended in freezing the gas near its source could be recovered when the liquid is re-vaporized. This was envisaged by the original pioneers of liquid methane transport, but in practice it is difficult to achieve.

Coldness is a commodity which is not easily transported over a long distance, so one can only utilize it by some industrial installation closely adjacent to the reception terminal. The cold generated at Canvey Island is some eighty times the total amount needed by the whole of Britain's frozen food industry. Used in another way it could generate 3500 tons of liquid oxygen per day. Instead of this it is put into the estuary waters, where it does something to lower their temperature and counter the heating effect of the electricity power stations upstream.

The yawning gap which exists between theoretical possibilities and practical achievement is no new experience for the fuel technologist. For example, most of the electricity generating stations waste more than half of the energy they consume, usually putting it into the waters of the river or creek by which they stand. The low-temperature heat they discard could be used for a number of industrial applications, or for the heating of dwellings, but it is far from easy to devise a way of doing this which does not entail enormous capital expenditure.

However, even if (for the time being at least) one is reconciled to the loss of this refrigerating energy at the methane receiving station, transport by tanker is still a good commercial proposition provided that:

(*a*) The quantity of gas is large (the two British ships will bring in 100 million cubic feet of gas per day—about 10 per cent of the average national usage);

(*b*) The price at the well head is low. The methane tanker is essentially a method of making use of gas which would otherwise be unused or wasted, and it depends for its commercial success on a low price at source.

(*c*) The distance travelled by the ships must be considerable—at about 1500 miles the cost compares well with that of a pipeline. If you have once liquefied your gas it pays you to take it as far as possible! On shorter distances it might still be workable if there were real difficulties in laying a pipeline.

(*d*) The boats must travel fast, and must turn round quickly at each port. The tanker is so expensive to construct and operate that it must be fully used and must carry as much cargo as possible in a given time.

OTHER LIQUID METHANE SCHEMES

The French gas industry will take a further 50 million cubic feet per day from the liquefaction plant at Arzew. Their new tanker, the *Jules Verne*, started regular operation in 1965, and carries its cargo to a new terminal at Le Havre. From here the gas is conveyed by a new pipeline towards Paris, passing on its way an underground storage site at St Illiers, near the small town of Verno on the Seine. Here an aquifer (see Chapter 4) has been constructed which will enable the natural gas from the Sahara to be reinterred in the rocks near Paris. This will enable Gaz de France to use its tanker and its pipeline uniformly throughout the year, storing gas when supply exceeds demand and bringing it out again when demand exceeds supply.

What will happen after this is not yet certain. Probably another tanker will be built, and another 50 million cu. ft/day liquefaction plant will be built at Arzew to supply it. By 1975 Paris will probably be supplied with natural gas unconverted, but in the immediate future all the gas imported will be either cracked (reduced to coal gas calorific value) or will be used to enrich lean gas made from petroleum products by the methods discussed at the end of Chapter 2.

It is most unlikely that this will be the end. A large liquefaction plant is to be constructed in Libya to process the gas found in that part of the Sahara. The distance from that country to Britain is much farther than from Algeria, but the sea route to Italy, France, and Spain will almost certainly be brought into use for this purpose.

Nigeria may also be exporting liquid methane before long. To make this an economic proposition, tankers larger than those built for the Arzew–London run will be needed.

Still farther afield there are large amounts of natural gas which are either being burnt to waste, for lack of a market, or else pumped into underground reservoirs pending an opportunity of selling. One thinks of the Middle East (Persia, Iraq, Persian Gulf) where a huge amount of gas brought up with the oil is still wasted. The amount burned to waste in this area is estimated at two and a half times the total gas consumption of Great Britain.

Venezuela is another country which has gas to dispose of. At one time they burned to waste more than the gas consumption of France; recent reports say that this has been reduced by the expedient of pumping the gas back into partly exhausted gas or oil wells. If the Sahara gas fields at Hassi-er-R'Mel had not been discovered, the British gas industry might have drawn its gas from Venezuela. As the natural gas resources of the United States are used up (and they are being consumed at a tremendous rate) it is far from impossible that tankers may carry liquefied methane from Venezuela to the East coast of North America, and from Alaska to the Pacific coast.

From a long-distance point of view, as citizens of the world, we must hope very much that these schemes are put into effect. Mankind has only the limited resources of the earth's thin crust to draw upon for fuel, and it seems a sin against the human race to squander these resources by burning them to waste. However plentiful they are today, the situation may be very different in 100 or 200 years' time. If we are the sort of people who feel a responsibility towards posterity, we should try to prevent it from suffering as a result of our negligence.

PLATE 11. Snaking-in.
(*By courtesy of William Press Ltd.*)

PLATE 12. The scene in the Sahara Desert at Hassi-er-R'Mel. The three flare pipes in the background are burning-off unwanted gas, but a much larger quantity is being sent by pipeline to the coast.

6 | Non-poisonous and Sulphur-free Gas

In September 1958 the International Gas Union was having its seventh three-yearly meeting in Rome. On these occasions many hundreds of gas engineers, chemists, and administrators from all over the world gather together. Many of them bring their ladies, and in addition to the formal technical meetings, excursions to places of interest in the neighbourhood are usually arranged.

One of the interesting features of this particular Congress was a visit to the Pope's summer residence at Castelgondolfo. While they were there the whole Congress were granted an audience; they were addressed by Pope Pius XII in the central courtyard of the palace. Most of the delegates expected a few pious generalizations and a blessing; but they were surprised to find that the Pope was far more familiar with their industry than they had expected. In the course of some very pertinent remarks he touched on the processes for making town gas less poisonous, and expressed the hope that such techniques would be developed and extended. It was a social duty, he said, to reduce as far as possible the hazards in the use of a fuel which in every other respect was so useful and convenient.

Long before support came from this rather unexpected quarter, it had often been urged that efforts should be made to reduce the amount of carbon monoxide in town gas supply. The problem does not arise when natural gas is distributed, but gases based on coal or oil have always contained a certain amount of this undesirable component. We say "undesirable" because it is this constituent which makes coal gas poisonous. Pure coal gas contains at least $7\frac{1}{2}$ per cent, but the use of carburetted water-gas as a supplementary fuel gas had become more and more general during the second quarter of the century. At times, when a large amount of this gas was being added, the carbon monoxide content of the final mixture might rise to 18 per cent or even exceed 20 per cent. These occasions naturally tend to arise when the weather is coldest. Unfortunately these are times when windows and doors are shut most tightly against the cold, and a gas leak can therefore do the most damage.

A leak of any combustible gas—or combustible liquid, for that matter—is a serious matter, quite apart from its toxicity. However, ordinary town gas cannot cause an explosion until about 6 per cent is present in the atmosphere. If the gas contains much carbon monoxide the toxicity hazard will arise at a much lower concentration. For example, if the town gas supply contains 20 per cent of CO, a $\frac{1}{2}$ per cent concentration will give 0·1 per cent CO in the air. This would normally cause unconsciousness if a person breathed it for an hour; a longer exposure would probably prove fatal. Even $\frac{1}{4}$ per cent town gas (0·05 per cent CO) could be fatal if exposure was prolonged. Normally, of course, this would not happen, for the smell would warn anyone inhaling the gas long before serious consequences could ensue.

Obviously if the carbon monoxide content is reduced to about 2 per cent this raises the critical concentration of town gas in air from 0·5 to 5 per cent. Beyond this we soon begin to approach the point at which the leak may result in an explosion before it becomes toxic. The poisoning hazard would be virtually eliminated if the CO could be reduced to 1 or 2 per cent; even a reduction to 5 per cent would make a very big improvement. The cost of the process must be taken into account, and the Gas Council (Great Britain) has announced that all new plant will aim at producing gas with less than 5 per cent carbon monoxide. This is the aim of the International Gas Union also.

CARBON MONOXIDE HAZARD

Carbon monoxide is a colourless, odourless gas which causes something like asphyxia when it is present in the air breathed by man—or by any warm-blooded animal. This is because it combines with the haemoglobin of the blood and prevents it from fulfilling its normal function—that of carrying oxygen from the lungs to the tissues of the body.

Carbon monoxide has about 300 times greater affinity for haemoglobin than has oxygen. It follows that even when far more oxygen

than carbon monoxide is present in the air, a considerable proportion of the blood becomes useless for the carriage of oxygen. The
ratio is known quite exactly; for instance, air containing 0·03 per

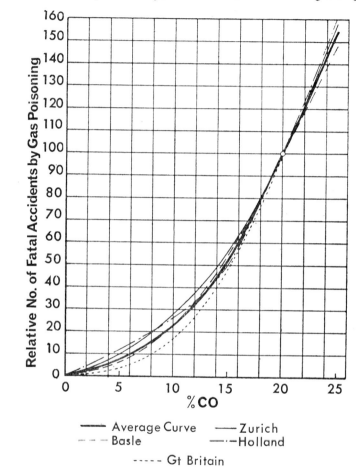

Fig. 21. The incidence of gas poisoning cases (on an arbitrary scale)
in relation to % CO in gas supplied.

cent of CO will eventually cause the blood to become 30 per cent
saturated with it if one breathes it for many hours.

With 30 per cent of the haemoglobin in the blood made useless,
the person will feel quite ill, and have a bad headache; in the 40 to

50 per cent range he becomes unconscious, and may die if not rescued. Once taken into fresh air, he may well make a complete recovery in quite a short time; provided he is still breathing, the CO saturation of the blood will steadily fall as air free of CO passes through his lungs. If breathing has stopped, artificial respiration may save him.

These characteristics show how different is carbon monoxide from an ordinary poison. The danger of exposure to carbon monoxide is roughly estimated by multiplying the time of exposure (in hours) by the concentration (in per cent). If this product exceeds 0·15 a fatality may occur. Thus, a concentration of 0·05 per cent, which would probably cause death if breathed for 3 or 4 hours, would be perfectly safe for $\frac{1}{2}$ hour.

Carbon monoxide is found very widely; it usually comes from the incomplete combustion of substances containing carbon. The exhaust gases from a motor car may contain 5 per cent or more; firemen are often overcome by carbon monoxide in the smoke from smouldering wood, cloth, or paper. Men working at a blast furnace have to be particularly careful, for the gas produced there contains a high percentage and is practically without smell. The solid-fuel kitchen boiler or the domestic oil stove can both be the cause of carbon monoxide poisoning accidents.

In the case of town gas, great care is taken to ensure that there is a strong smell to warn any persons that gas is escaping. The old-style coal gas has such a smell without needing any additives; gas from modern plants is 'odorized' by the addition of minute amounts of strongly smelling organic substances. Unfortunately, of course, some elderly people have a poor sense of smell. Such people are the most likely to suffer from home accidents of all kinds.

Even before any steps were taken to reduce the carbon monoxide content of town gas, gas poisoning was not a very frequent cause of accident. In 1947, for instance, the total number of accidental deaths in Britain was 349 for every million persons in the population: 114 of these were attributed to transport accidents, 103 to falling, drowning accounted for 27, suffocation for 25, burns for 19, and coal gas poisoning for only 9.

A reduction in carbon monoxide content will greatly reduce the gas poisoning rate. Some statistics produced at the Eighth International Gas Union Congress (Stockholm, 1961) showed that the accident rate falls much more rapidly even than one might expect:

if 20 per cent CO causes 100 accidents,

then:
15 per cent	causes	50 accidents
10 per cent	causes	20 accidents
5 per cent	causes	5 accidents
2 per cent	causes	1 accident

It is clear that the gas industry's target of "5 per cent or less" is going to represent a big improvement in safety. The curves on which these figures (Fig. 21) were based came from Switzerland, Holland, and Great Britain, and the results are very similar.

DETOXIFICATION OF COAL GAS AND WATER-GAS

The town of Hameln in Germany (the Hamelin of Browning's Pied Piper, "by famous Hanover city") was the pioneer in detoxification. In the years immediately preceding the Second World War they operated a plant to reduce the carbon monoxide in the gas made at the town gas works. Coming to more recent times, Basle in Switzerland was the first large city to remove carbon monoxide; it started this operation in 1958.

There are three principal ways of detoxifying town gas:

1. Chemical absorption
2. Hydrogenation over a catalyst
3. The addition of steam and 'shift-reaction' over a catalyst

Of these the third is by far the most important. The chemical absorption processes (1) make use of copper salts—at Winterthür in Switzerland a mixture of cuprous chloride and magnesium chloride has been used. This absorbs CO quite readily, but will give it up again if the liquid is heated gently under vacuum. The pure CO obtained in this way can be used as a fuel on the works.

Although this may sound simple, the absorption process has serious drawbacks. The last traces of oxygen must be removed before treatment—a fact which adds immediately to the complexity of the process. Another trouble is that by removing CO one raises the calorific value of the gas and lowers the density; then it is not interchangeable with the untreated gas.

The second method, hydrogenation, was developed in Germany at a time (about 1950) when the economic balance of fuels was much more favourable to coal. Then the possibility of making liquid hydrocarbons from coal was quite important; today it would hardly be considered. A German chemical works introduced the hydrogenation process, and found a use in its own factory for the oils produced. The detoxified gas was sold to a gas distribution company.

The process depends on the fact that hydrogen can be made to combine with carbon monoxide to produce methane and a number of heavier hydrocarbons, some of them liquid. To effect this change the gases must be passed over a special catalyst at 230°C. Unfortunately the catalyst is very sensitive to the deterioration caused by traces of certain impurities; unless these are removed it would soon cease to function. For this reason, and because of the change in the economic situation, the process is not used today.

Most practicable schemes today are based, like the original process at Hamelin, on the 'shift reaction' in the presence of steam. To explain this a short excursion into physical chemistry is necessary. The basic formula for the reaction is:

$$CO + H_2O \rightleftharpoons H_2 + CO_2 + 10,390 \text{ cal}$$

The important thing about this equation is that it can quite easily go both ways: from left to right or from right to left. If a large amount of H_2O (steam) or CO is present it tends to move to the right; if there is little H_2O or CO and much CO_2 and H_2 it tends to go from right to left.

Another important factor is the temperature; high temperatures favour carbon monoxide (i.e. the equation goes to the left) and low temperatures favour CO_2 (i.e. it goes to the right). Now, while this is true as regards the equilibrium condition, the actual speed of a reaction is a different matter. This reaction (like most reactions) goes only slowly at low temperatures and gets faster the higher the temperature. One might think therefore that the position was hopeless; for in order to get a fast reaction you need a high temperature, and then you get a high percentage of CO.

In this situation the phenomenon of catalysis again comes to our aid. As was explained earlier, catalysts do not alter the equilibrium which would eventually be obtained; what they do is to enable this equilibrium ratio to be reached very much more quickly. The reaction rate is speeded up enormously. In this case it has been found that, using a catalyst composed of iron oxide (with a trace of chromium oxide in it) one can make the steam–CO reaction go quite quickly even at a low temperature; 350° to 450°C is usually employed.

This, then, is the process at Basle. Steam is added to the gas before it enters the catalyst chamber, and once again it is necessary to guard the main chamber with a preliminary hydrogenating catalyst to remove substances which would otherwise cause poisoning. More steam must be added than is actually used up in the reaction chamber, and the surplus must be condensed from the outgoing gas. In addition, it is necessary to remove the trace of hydrogen sulphide which comes from the hydrogenation of organic sulphur compounds (to be discussed later in this chapter).

It is not surprising, perhaps, that the advantages of non-poisonous gas are not obtained without some financial sacrifice. The cost to the citizens of Basle was an increase in price of between 6 and 9 per cent. More recent writers have claimed that the cost of the process is less than this, however; and this is due to yet another shift in the economics of gas making. The rich hydrocarbon gases, such as methane, propane, and butane, are now cheaper (per unit of heat) than the lean gases, such as water gas. In the coal-gas era the reverse was true, but the enormous increase in oil refining in western Europe, and the discovery of fresh natural gas fields, have made hydrocarbon gases much more plentiful, and therefore cheaper.

The shift reaction appears at first glance to give no change in volume:

$$1 \text{ vol. } CO + 1 \text{ vol. steam} \rightarrow 1 \text{ vol. } H_2 + 1 \text{ vol. } CO_2$$

but as the steam must be added to the gas, the reaction actually causes an increase in volume. Since the total heat content also falls slightly this means that the heat content per unit volume, or calorific value, drops considerably. One can restore it to the accustomed value either by removing the CO_2 or by adding a rich hydrocarbon gas; the latter alternative is much more economical, for it makes use of a relatively cheap source of energy. The removal of all the CO_2 is also undesirable for a different reason: the final product is then a gas so rich in hydrogen that it has a lower density than usual, and hence is not suitable for ordinary use. It is safe to say that detoxification today should cost less than the price paid by the people of Basle.

DETOXIFICATION OF HIGH-PRESSURE GAS

The preceding discussion has all been related to gas made from coal and coke—the classical methods of making gas. But, as we saw in Chapter 2, these are being superseded by high-pressure techniques —gasifiers such as the Lurgi using low-grade coal, and (much more important) plant for making gas from petroleum fractions.

In this type of plant, detoxification can be achieved much more simply and cheaply. This is partly because, when a process is carried out at high pressure, the vessels can be so much smaller. Another reason is that steam is nearly always used in the gasification process; the surplus steam left in the gas is then available for the shift reaction chamber. Catalysts have been developed which can be used on the hot impure gases as they come straight from the Lurgi gasification stage; this has the advantage that all the H_2S can be taken out at once. Practically all new high-pressure gasification plants, whether for coal or oil, incorporate a shift-reaction stage and deliver gas having less than 5 per cent CO.

REMOVAL OF ORGANIC SULPHUR

Most of the sulphur in coal gas and water gas is in the form of hydrogen sulphide, H_2S—a corrosive, evil-smelling, and very poisonous gas which we all associate with our early impressions of the school chemical laboratory. In Chapter 2 we described briefly the classical method of removing H_2S by iron oxide which is spread out on wooden trays in steel purifier boxes.

It has been recognized for a century or more that the removal of this impurity from town gas is essential. Not only would the H_2S corrode metal fittings carrying the gas—particularly those made of brass or copper—but also it produces sulphur dioxide (and a little trioxide) when the gas is burned. Sulphur dioxide (SO_2) is far less poisonous than H_2S but it is still an unpleasant gas to breathe, being a severe irritant to the mucous membranes. Sulphur dioxide in the products of combustion also causes severe corrosion to gas appliances, particularly water heaters.

One can safely say that no reputable gas undertaking has or will send out gas for domestic use that contains any perceptible amount of H_2S, but unfortunately there is another source of sulphur which is less easy to remove. This is the organic sulphur compounds, usually one of three substances, or groups of substances:

Mercaptans; methyl (CH_3—SH) and ethyl (CH_3—CH_2—SH)

Thiophenes; C_4H_4S (cyclic) and related substances

Carbon oxy-sulphide; COS

These are not removed by iron oxide and together they are present in conventional coal gas supplies to the extent of about 300 milligrammes per cubic metre (in Britain).

Organic sulphur compounds have the great disadvantage that they burn to produce sulphur oxides, the dioxide SO_2, and a certain amount of trioxide SO_3, which is even more objectionable. These form sulphurous and sulphuric acids respectively when dissolved in water, and these two acids are principally responsible for the corrosion which occurs in (for example) a domestic water heater. If liberated into the atmosphere they can cause the fading of fabrics and deterioration of leather; they are also responsible for the very slight smell associated with the products of combustion of town gas. (Perhaps it is more of a taste than a smell.)

Methods for removing organic sulphur have long been known. The amount can be reduced considerably by intensive agitation with oil; it can be removed almost completely by passing the gas through active carbon. Passing coal gas through a catalyst chamber can remove organic sulphur compounds by adding hydrogen to them, and producing H_2S; this can be removed by conventional means.

All these techniques are expensive, however, and until recently it did not seem worth making this improvement in gas quality as it involved a marked increase in price. In this respect also the outlook is improving. The new high-pressure gasification processes nearly all produce a gas which is free of organic sulphur compounds. As we have seen in Chapter 3, the catalyst chamber for the main gas-making process is preceded by a sulphur-removal stage in which the organic sulphur compounds are made to combine with hydrogen. Layers of zinc oxide, placed in the same vessel, absorb the H_2S as soon as it is formed.

Similarly, the hydrogenation catalyst which is used at the entrance to the shift-reaction stage in the detoxification of town gas reacts with organic sulphur compounds, and so a sulphur-free gas is obtained from coal gas, as well as one which is no longer toxic.

This chapter has been devoted to some of the less spectacular ways in which the gas supply to home and factory can be improved in quality. Although this improvement is already taking place as these lines are written, it must inevitably be many years before it affects every gas undertaking. Now, however, they have a target: the production of non-toxic and sulphur-free gas is within sight. The social duty to reduce as far as possible the hazards in the use of this fuel is being fulfilled.

7 | Patterns of Organization

GREAT BRITAIN

The gas industry in Britain began as a number of small, isolated competing private companies. They supplied anyone with gas who asked for it and who could conveniently be connected to their main; several companies might operate in the same area. It is recorded, for example, that at one time the gas pipes of eight different competing companies were to be found under Whitehall (in the centre of Westminster).

The savage competition between the small overlapping companies of this period is something which bears little relation to the dignified behaviour of the modern gas undertaking. For example, it was quite possible that a potential customer, when he approached Company A to ask for a service, would be quietly connected to the gas mains of Company B. As a result, Company B supplied the gas and Company A was paid for it.

If a main-laying gang was caught perpetrating such an act of robbery, the employees of the rival company were apt to act first and argue afterwards. It was not uncommon for the dispute to end in a bloody fight with pick and shovel between rival groups of service layers. One chronicler remarks that "in spite of the intense competition, gas was not cheap"—and one can easily believe this. (Even in a modern undertaking, the cost of distributing gas by pipes under the street adds several pence to the cost of each therm of gas.) A system to give monopoly rights over an area to one company was introduced in 1860. Although there was much protest at the time, it is easy to see now that this was really a most necessary step in the industry's development.

A similar pattern was followed in other parts of the world where gas companies sprang up. The next development was the acquisition of some of these companies by the local authority—especially in the large industrial towns. Most of the large towns of Britain (with the notable exception of London) operated their gas undertaking as a municipal department up to the date of nationalization. London, however, was supplied by a number of gas companies. The largest of these, the Gas, Light and Coke Co. Ltd., was a direct successor of the first gas company in the world, the Gas Light Company of Westminster, founded in 1812.

In Britain, prior to nationalization in 1949, there were nearly 1000 separate gas undertakings. It is true there were several groups each belonging to a holding company—in the Severn Valley, for instance, in south-east England, and in the West Riding. These groups, while they represented an improvement by offering facilities for co-ordinated management and scientific control, were often in patchwork patterns on the map, and geographically far from ideal. Municipal gas departments were often even less co-ordinated; for example, there was no connecting gas main between Stockton-on-Tees and Middlesbrough, whose centres are some 5 miles apart.

The Gas Act of 1948 nationalized the British gas industry and, by general consent, was one of the most successful of the big changes in industrial organization set in motion by the Government of that day. A measure of compulsory integration and co-ordination was clearly needed, and in most cases it brought a far better service to the customer once the initial disorganization had been passed.

The Act divided England, Scotland, and Wales into twelve areas, each under the control of an area gas board. Scotland and Wales each formed a single area—an act of deference to Celtic nationalist feeling perhaps, for the Coal Mines Act a year or two before had attached North Wales to Lancashire and South Wales to Somerset and the Forest of Dean. Fig. 22 shows the gas map of England as it is today.

A distinctive feature of the Act was that it provided no strong central authority; the twelve area boards were expressly charged to behave as autonomous regions. However, in order to provide for some co-ordination between these sovereign states, the Gas Council was provided, on which there was a seat for each area board chairman. In addition, two official members were appointed: a chairman and vice-chairman whose duty was to assist in securing co-ordination. This was a rather weak form of central organization, and probably represented a reaction to the many criticisms levelled against the

Fig. 22. The gas map of Britain. The administrative areas are: 1. Scottish, 2. Northern, 3. North-Western, 4. North-Eastern, 5. East Midlands, 6. West Midlands, 7. Wales, 8. Eastern, 9. North Thames, 10. South Eastern, 11. Southern, 12. South-Western.

nationalization a year or two earlier of the coal mines; opponents of that measure had complained that the National Coal Board was "vast", "unwieldy", "monolithic", and bound to be out of touch with day-to-day mining problems.

The structure chosen also reflected the nature of the gas industry in 1948. At that time gas supplies normally came from a gas works a few miles distant. Long-distance transmission lines were practically unknown in Britain, save for a collecting system taking coke oven gas from the coke ovens to the big towns in south Yorkshire. It was probably not at all apparent at that time to the drafters of the Act that planning on a national scale would soon become necessary. By organizing it regionally they hoped also to avoid the disadvantage of a centralized bureaucracy, which can easily be remote and unfeeling.

There can be little doubt that, for the first five years or so, this policy was a success. The immediate need was for local co-ordination. Stockton-on-Tees and Middlesbrough have been already mentioned above; one of the first acts of the newly formed Northern Gas Board was to construct a pipeline between these two towns and to arrange for the extensions needed in productive plant to be all concentrated in one site.

The newly formed area boards soon set to work to rationalize gas production by closing down the small and uneconomic works and concentrating production in a few sites where gas could be made as cheaply as possible. This in turn necessitated a pipeline grid over the area, linking the production sites with the centres of population. In the first ten years most of the boards constructed the network of pipelines needed to integrate their area and supply it with gas made at the lowest price possible, and of uniform quality.

WEAKNESSES OF THE GAS ACT

By this time a map of the gas distribution system in Britain began to look rather like a pattern of pressed leaves. Large arteries linked the main centres in each area, and the pipelines became smaller and smaller as they approached the border. No gas crossed the frontiers. It became clear that something more than regional planning was needed. Under the Gas Act each area board had been given the monopoly right to carry and to sell gas in their territory. It seemed to be nobody's business to arrange that one area, having too much, should sell to another area which had too little. There was no national pipeline system.

The need for a stronger hand in national planning was also emphasized by technical developments. The Gas Council had been searching for sites for underground storage (as described in Chapter 4), and had found a number of suitable areas. Obviously such a development would have to be arranged to benefit the country as a whole, and could not be limited to the particular Gas Board in whose territory it lay.

Even more compelling was the development of the project for liquid methane importation. This demanded the construction of a pipeline system to carry natural gas from the Thames estuary to Manchester and Leeds, with branches supplying other big cities on the way. It stands to the credit of the gas industry that, in spite of the weakness of the central organization on paper, informal collaboration between the areas was so good that this network could be constructed. Each area board organized the laying of the stretch lying in its own land.

By this time it was obvious that more power must be given to a national authority, and a Select Committee of the House of Commons reported in 1961 that either a thirteenth board should be set up with powers to sell, manufacture, and transport gas on a national scale, or else the powers of the existing Gas Council should be increased to enable them to perform this function. In the Gas Act (1965) the second of these alternatives was embodied in British law.

Another difficulty with the Gas Act of 1948 was the problem of appointing the boards. Not only the main administrative boards, but also the consultative councils set up in each region to effect some co-ordination between the gas undertaking and the consumer, were covered by the phrase "The Minister shall appoint". Out of the several hundreds of appointments made, not one was made by the process of democratic election.

Some people thought that one at least of the members of each board might be elected by the employees, to represent their interests. However, an amendment to this effect, inserted by the House of Lords, was deleted again when the Bill returned to the Commons. Absolute power of appointment was left in the hands of the Minister of Fuel. While a great many excellent administrators were appointed, the Minister's efforts were not uniformly successful—and indeed this is hardly surprising.

PRODUCTION, DISTRIBUTION, SALES

A feature of the gas industry's organization which sometimes surprises newcomers is the way in which it tends to be divided into three compartments. The gas manufacturing station forms a unit in itself, responsible directly to the Board. The distribution department takes over the gas as it leaves the works, and conveys it by pipe, storage, and governor to the customer's gas meter. At this point it leaves the distribution department and comes into the province of the Sales Department.

In the old days these three departments were divided by bulkheads which—if not gastight—were almost watertight. Each division knew little of what went on in the other two, and only very rarely would any employee pass from one to the other. There was sometimes a tendency for the gasworks engineer to think his job was over once the gas had left his province (a very high brick wall still encircles many of the older works). Since the gasworks engineer was the aristocrat of the profession, he was apt to place the blame on the Sales Department if complaints arose at the customer's end of the pipe. In some undertakings the engineers in charge of gas making were only persuaded with difficulty that they must take account of variations in flame characteristics when they introduced new processes at the works.

The present trends are rapidly breaking up this rigid old hierarchical system. For one reason, the gas-making station, as a local institution, may no longer exist—the gas may be piped from 50 miles away. Another factor is that the increasing size of the gas distribution network (even within the area board boundary) has forced the interchangeability problem into the foreground. If a customer is liable to receive his gas supply from one of several widely separated sources, it is more than ever necessary to insist on a uniform combustion characteristic. This means the gas maker and the gas user must work in closer contact than ever before.

BELGIUM

Up to 1914 Belgium had a similar system to that in Britain. Each town or city had one or more gasworks, supplying gas to the

PLATE 13. The methane liquefaction plant at Arzew. Three of the above-ground tanks for storing liquid methane can be seen to the rear of the picture, and between two of them is the jetty at which the liquid methane tankers are loaded. The rectangular building in the foreground holds the compressors which are used in the liquefaction process.

PLATE 14. The Canvey Island reception station for liquefied natural gas from Algiers.

(*By courtesy of the Gas Council*)

immediate locality. It was under the control either of a municipal department or a private company, and it took responsibility for the whole system, from the intake of coal at the works to the maintenance of cookers in the people's homes.

In 1919 Belgium was in a sorry state. For four years its land had been fought over, and vast destruction had been caused. As for its gas industry, hardly any of the original gasworks were in a condition to go into operation at all. This disaster brought about a change in the whole structure of the industry which probably gave it benefit in the long run.

A number of coke-oven plants were standing, and it was of vital importance to operate them so that coke for the metallurgical industries and gas for the chemical industries could be produced. The decision was taken to abandon nearly all the small gasworks and concentrate coal carbonization in the coke-oven plants. These produced enough coal gas to supply, if properly distributed, all the needs of the gas users in the country.

From that date the gas industry in Belgium virtually ceased to make gas; it became a purchaser. It would have been absurd for each local undertaking to send its own pipelines out to the coke ovens, so a new type of company—the pipeline company—was formed. The pipeline companies bought the gas that was available from the coke ovens at a price agreed between the two parties, and built pipeline networks to enable them to sell gas to the municipalities and other local undertakings.

Thus was born a system which, as we have just seen, was missing in Britain. It seems to have served Belgium well; though we must remember that the amount of gas used, per head of population, is much lower than in Britain. The several pipeline companies co-operated and ultimately combined to form the Distrigaz Company; this continues to serve as a most efficient middle-man and transport agent for the Belgian gas industry. There is a second pipeline company, the Savgaz Company, which works in collaboration with it.

In their search for more gas, Distrigaz have often been very enterprising. As an example, in the years following the Second World War they turned their attention to the use of mine gas obtained from the system of methane drainage. One coal mine after another agreed to supply Distrigaz with firedamp, and a collecting grid was built in the coal-mining district lying between Mons and Charleroi

for the purpose of conveying this firedamp to a central processing
station at the St Aldegonde mine (near Binche). At one time thirty
separate mines were linked up in this system, and were supplying
10 per cent of the gas used in Belgium.

In this matter Belgium led the world (although the Saar territory
was also very advanced), and it may be conjectured that the existence

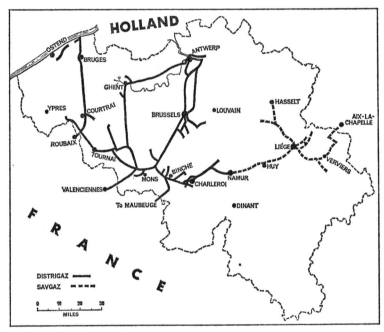

Fig. 23. Gas distribution map of Belgium. These pipelines carry town
gas; the methane grid is not shown. The main source of town gas is
the coke ovens situated on the coalfields around Mons.

of a pipeline company willing and eager to buy contributed largely
to this progressive development.

More recently the Distrigaz Company has been making great use
of the L.P. gases, and has constructed large underground caverns in
the clay under Antwerp harbour in which to store them in liquid
form. By this means they were able to buy when the price was
lowest, and sell (as gas) when demand was greatest. This development was not carried so far as originally intended, because of the
possible arrival of Dutch natural gas. By the time this book is in

print, Distrigaz may have begun to distribute Slochteren natural gas to the Belgian cities.

GERMANY

The German Federal Republic occupies a place somewhat midway between that of Britain and Belgium. Like Britain, it possesses a number of large gas-making stations, especially those attached to the big cities. At the same time, it has a very large pipeline company, the Ruhrgas Co., which performs a similar function to Distrigaz in Belgium.

The Ruhrgas Co. and its associates extend their network from Hanover (where they built the first European aquifer) down to Cologne, Frankfurt, Dortmund (where they have a second aquifer) and on to Baden-Baden. The Saarferngas Co., which is associated with it, brings gas along the Moselle valley from the Saar coke ovens, and a new line is being built to run from the Rhine eastwards, north of Munich, to the 'iron curtain' frontier.

At Dorsten, near Cologne, is one of the largest batteries of Lurgi gasifiers in the world. These are fed with brown coal (lignite) which occurs very plentifully near there, and the gas produced is enriched either with L.P. gas or with natural gas brought by pipeline from the Ems estuary. The Dorsten plant is owned by the Ruhrgas Co., and it helps to supply their vast network, supplementing the coke oven gas bought in the Ruhr valley. Germany will soon be importing natural gas from Holland.

The German gas undertakings either make their own gas, or buy it from the pipeline company, or do both together.

FRANCE

France nationalized its gas industry after the Second World War and chose a rather different plan from that adopted in Britain. A single statutory authority, Gaz de France, was set up, with head-quarters in Paris, divided for administrative purposes into geographical and also functional sections.

The central organization is controlled by a tripartite board, which purports to represent in equal numbers (*a*) gas technologists, (*b*) gas employees, and (*c*) gas consumers. The existence of a national authority has enabled France to make many bold strokes of policy which gas engineers north of the Channel must have looked at with envy.

One such project was the construction of a 300-mile pipeline to bring coke oven gas from Lorraine and the Saar to Paris. Together with this pipeline there soon followed France's first underground

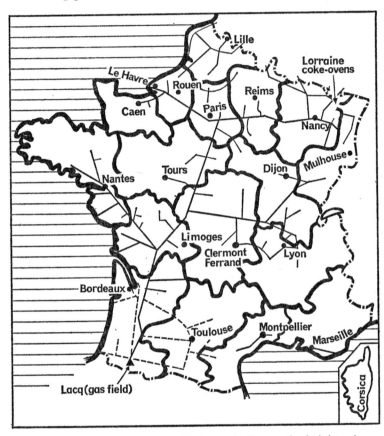

Fig. 24. Map showing the principal gas pipelines and administrative areas of France. The coal gas comes mostly from the coke ovens in Lorraine, and the natural gas from Lacq. The broken lines represent the network owned by the Compagnie Française de Methane, which is partly controlled by Gaz de France.

storage system, at Beynes near Versailles. Here, within striking distance of the great metropolis, it was possible to store all the gas brought from Lorraine during the summer, and use it subsequently to fulfil the heaviest of winter demands. The aquifer at Beynes enabled the very expensive pipeline to be used at the same rate throughout the year—another very important consideration economically.

When the large natural gas field at Lacq, near Pau in the foothills of the Pyrenees, was discovered, Gaz de France had to tackle the very difficult technical problem of getting it under control and organizing its commercial exploitation. They built extensive well-head plant for removing the high percentage of H_2S and also the valuable L.P. gas component. Then began the construction of a new system of pipelines across France superimposed on the old pattern. The new pipes carried the gas to a new aquifer at Lussagnet, nearby, and from here they fanned out to Nantes on the Bay of Biscay (subsequently extended to Rennes), to Paris, and to Lyons and Grenoble.

At one time it seemed that Gaz de France would lay a pipeline (or a series of pipes) across the Mediterranean from Algeria to Spain, so that natural gas from the Sahara could be brought to France. For various reasons (not least the technical difficulties: the sea is $1\frac{1}{2}$ miles deep) this project has been abandoned for the time being, and the Gaz de France methane tanker, the *Jules Verne*, now brings liquid methane from Algeria to Le Havre—whence a pipeline conveys it to Paris up the Seine valley. An aquifer between Paris and Rouen (France's third) is being used to even out the load.

UNITED STATES OF AMERICA

In the U.S.A., as one might expect, the development pattern has been based very much on private enterprise. There are some municipal undertakings, but these only handle about 5 per cent of the total gas sales, the remainder being supplied by Companies. For example, in New York the central and northern districts are supplied by the Consolidated Edison Co., and the southern part (Brooklyn, Richmond, etc.) by the Brooklyn Union Gas Co.

While these supply (or 'utility') companies are private, in the sense that capital is subscribed by individuals who may receive dividends in return, their operation is controlled quite firmly by governmental agencies. In most of the states there is a Public Utilities Commission staffed by permanent civil servants under the State Legislature, and this keeps a firm check on the rate of profit. If this exceeds the permitted maximum—usually $6\frac{1}{2}$ per cent—the Commission may require that the price of gas be lowered.

Although these are private companies, it does not follow that a new gas company could start operating in the middle of a big city. The Public Utilities Commission will have already granted exclusive rights ('franchise') to the Company which operates there, and no other body may infringe them. If a new company is to be set up to supply an area where there is no existing franchise, another body, the Federal Power Commission (dealing with the whole of the U.S.A.), must be consulted and given full details of the service it is proposed to give. It must also state the price it proposes to charge, and this must be approved by the State Public Utilities Commission.

The Public Utilities Commission also acts as kind of court, for anyone may appeal to it if he thinks he is not being treated fairly by the existing Company.

The supply companies normally buy their gas from a pipeline company, which is also run on private enterprise lines. The United States is covered with a fine network of pipelines which serves to connect the wells with the centres of population in which the gas is consumed. For example, taking New York again, most of the gas is brought in by three pipeline companies. The largest of these, Transco, has two parallel pipelines, 36 inches and 30 inches in diameter. Transco, in turn, buys gas from a large number of gas producing wells, the farthest away of which are right on the Mexican border (near Brownsville) 1800 miles distant.

The main centres of gas production have gradually moved farther south as the wells nearer to the eastern seaboard have been exhausted. Many of the depleted wells in Pennsylvania and West Virginia are now used as storage fields, taking in gas during the summer so that it can be withdrawn again in winter when the demand is greatest.

The gigantic 'Panhandle' field in Texas still yields a large volume of gas, but the newer wells are mostly situated either on the Gulf of Mexico coast (around New Orleans and westward to the Mexico border) or are actually out at sea, in the shallow waters of the continental shelf (Fig. 8, Chapter 3).

New York has been taken as an example, but all the large centres of population are supplied with natural gas in a similar way. Canadian natural gas supplements the home-produced fuel in the north and north-west of the country; and Vermont, in the north-east, will soon be supplied. A very small amount of gas is still made from coal, but this only amounts to about 0·2 per cent.

Pipeline companies, too, are regulated by the Government. The Federal Power Commission must give permission before any pipeline running across State borders is built. It also regulates the price structure and the rate at which profit is earned. In some cases where a community wants to receive a gas supply, but a pipeline would not be an economic proposition, the Federal Government in Washington can authorize a grant of money to enable the pipe to be built.

Endowed with quite exceptional resources of natural gas, and also a severe continental climate, the U.S.A. has been able in this way to build up a far bigger usage of gas per head than any other country in the world. In addition to the ordinary domestic purposes it is very widely used for house heating and house cooling. Outside the house it is used for barbecues and for radiant heating in courtyards and balconies; here, too, gas lighting is (very surprisingly) being widely used and swimming pools are heated by gas.

Gas is also used for power in the U.S.A., especially in the south, where it is widely used for irrigation pumps. One supply company in this region sells one third of its total output for this purpose.

An important role is played by the American Gas Association (A.G.A.), a voluntary body to which nearly all the pipeline companies and supply companies adhere; manufacturers of gas-burning appliances are also associated with it. It sponsors a great deal of research work, some of which is carried out in its own laboratories and some is assigned to other institutions.

At its testing laboratories in Cleveland, Ohio, and Los Angeles, California, gas appliances are examined to see if they can be permitted to carry the coveted blue star badge which indicates A.G.A. approval. An appliance model normally retains this badge for a period of five years, but this is subject to satisfactory reports from the A.G.A. inspectors who go out at least twice a year to the maker's factory. It is their job to see that the performance and safety requirements are still being complied with, and that quality is being maintained on the daily production line.

SOVIET UNION

The Russian gas industry was very small until quite recently. In 1917 only 11,000 apartments in Moscow were supplied with gas; this is a far smaller number than would be expected by comparison with other cities of similar size and importance in Europe. Even in 1940 the number was only 62,000. The gas supplied was mainly made from coal; it was however mixed with richer gas from an oil refinery. It was during the Second World War that the first important

Fig. 25

discovery of natural gas was made, at Saratov, a Volga town some 450 miles to the south-west of Moscow—an epoch-making event for the Soviet Union. (Fig. 25.)

From this time onwards the gas industry began to grow at an amazing speed. A pipeline was constructed in 1946 to take the Saratov gas to the capital, and in 1948 a new gas field in the former

Polish territories, near Lvov, was opened up, and a supply was run from it to Kiev. However, the most significant advance was in 1956 and 1957: this corresponded with the discovery of two much bigger gas fields in the lands lying to the north of the Black Sea, at Shebelinka and Stavropol.

In the following years many other sources of natural gas were discovered, so that now Moscow is fed from the west, the south-west, and the south-east by three separate long-distance mains, the one from the south being laid in triplicate. Round the outskirts of Moscow runs a ring-main connecting them all together.

One advantage of such a network is that short-term storage of gas can be largely dispensed with. The many sources of gas give a high degree of reliability, and the long lengths of main represent a considerable storage capacity in themselves.[1] By 1963 the number of households receiving gas in Moscow had reached over a million (a sixteen-fold increase over 1940), with 450,000 in Leningrad and 215,000 in Kiev.

The largest gas field in Russia, and the fourth largest in the world, is at Gazli, near Bokhara. This is in the extreme south of the Soviet Union, east of the Caspian and south of the Aral Sea. The gas lies in a very porous stratum, and relatively close to the surface of the ground, so that extraction can be achieved by boreholes which are relatively few in number and are less deep than is usually necessary.

In its geographical location the gas field is not quite so convenient, for the main demand for a gaseous fuel lies in the industrial area of the Urals, some 1400 miles to the north. Between the two points of supply and demand stretches some of the most difficult country one can imagine—deserts of shifting sand in the south, barren rock plateaux on the west shore of the Aral Sea, and waterless semi-desert steppes farther north still. To lay a pipeline over such terrain was a most difficult task, and the fact that it was done successfully was a triumph of engineering skill. It is worth while pausing a moment to look at some of the more sensational features of the project.

The volume of gas which had to be carried was so great that a double line of pipes was constructed, and the largest-sized pipe available was used—40 inches diameter. The double line runs to

[1] Aquifer storage systems near the city help to even out the variations from season to season.

Cheliabinsk, on the eastern side of the Ural Mountains, and a single line continues north from this town to Sverdlovsk. The pipeline is

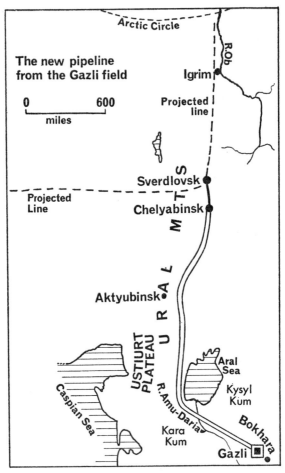

Fig. 26. Map of the double pipeline carrying natural gas from the Gazli field to the industrial centres lying on the eastern flank of the Ural mountains. The broken lines represent projected pipes for bringing gas from the newly discovered field at Igrim, in the north, and for supplying Moscow.

being continued further north, to link up with a big gas field at Igrim, on the River Ob (see Fig. 26). Further north still, the Yamal peninsula, inside the Arctic Circle, has still larger resources and no doubt before long the pipe will be extended to reach them. Sverdlovsk will send gas westwards towards Moscow by a new east-west pipeline which is likely to be built.

The story of the Bokhara–Cheliabinsk pipeline has some astonishing details. In the south the loose sandy desert surface had been piled up into ridges and it was necessary to level a wide strip by means of bulldozers before work could commence. The barren nature of the country made it possible to move far larger lengths of pipe than would have been feasible in a populated countryside; 120-foot lengths of 40-inch pipe were moved up into position on two tractors (a second one near the rear end). To reach points on the shore of the Aral Sea, water transport was used; the pipes were welded into 200-foot lengths, plugged at each end, and were towed floating. Fifteen of these lengths formed a sort of raft, and a ship-towed caravan would normally consist of a lake steamer towing three such rafts behind it.

On the other hand, for much of the route water was extremely scarce. The compressor stations which are placed at intervals along the pipeline must have cooling water, and in one case this had to be piped from a place 85 miles away! When the sand was very loose, attempts were made to consolidate the ground above the pipe by planting desert grass and bushes; to give them a chance to take root, a thin asphalt–water emulsion was sprayed on to the sand. Many rivers had to be crossed, the biggest being the Amu-Daria, which is one of the two large rivers running into the Aral Sea. Here a pipe bridge was constructed, with a span of 1150 feet, but in most other cases an underwater crossing was possible.

The Russian gas industry, as one would expect, is based entirely on government enterprise. The directive body, Gasprom, is one of the U.S.S.R. State Production Committees; this makes or extracts the gas and passes it on to local distribution undertakings, which are under the control of the local authority.

Partly, perhaps, on account of its very rapid rise, and also because of the very different political conditions in the Soviet Union, the gas industry in that country presents some striking contrasts with the western countries. For example, the proportion of gas supplied to domestic consumers is much lower—about 11 per cent (in Great Britain it is about 50 per cent). This is partly due to the large amount used in industry. The local boards distribute gas not only to homes, but also to metallurgical works, cement works, blast furnaces, and electric power stations.

This situation also probably accounts for the very large amount of gas consumed per head of inhabitant—it is considerably more than in Britain. (Considering the enormous area covered by the Soviet Union this is remarkable.) There is no doubt that the Russians are forging ahead to a state of affairs where—as in the United States and Canada—gas will be the principal fuel of the country. They have great natural resources lying below the surface of the very large area of territory, and they clearly intend to make full use of this. Their gas consumption has increased at a staggering rate over the past few years; the figures for Moscow, for instance, are:

	1945	1950	1955	1960	1963 (planned)
Million cubic metres per annum	69	272	456	719	1050

and it is planned that, by 1980, the national consumption will have become fifteen times the 1960 figure. Then, gas and oil together will account for two thirds of all the fuel consumption of the Soviet Union.

At the same time, human needs have much in common the world over. In 1960 the ratio of summer to winter consumption in the Soviet Union was only 1 to 1·3—to western eyes a surprisingly low figure, when one considers the severity of the winters. Four years later, however, a report to the International Gas Union stated that "in winter the daily gas consumption is almost twice as large as in summer". It seems that some of the problems of western countries are spreading to communist territory!

One of the ways of dealing with this problem (in a land of limitless natural gas) is deliberately to increase the use of gas in summer—for instance, by feeding it to the electric power stations. It can also be supplied to factories who are willing to change over to some alternative fuel at times of peak gas demand—a system which has been much developed in the United States. Underground storage is also of great assistance in levelling out the seasonal variations in demand.

8 | Flame

Zeus, it is said, brought the Golden Age to an end by his decision to make life on earth much more difficult for mankind. The Titan Prometheus, by way of recompense for hardships to come, gave man the gift of fire. What could he have given that would have been more valuable? The acquisition of fire must have been one of the most important landmarks in human progress, even more than the wheel, perhaps. It certainly enabled men to colonize parts of the world which would otherwise have been uninhabitable. Not only did it give him artificial warmth, but by enabling him to cook food-stuffs it greatly widened the range of edible substances available.

Small wonder, therefore, that even today flame has a degree of mystical significance for civilized man. One has only to consider the torch-carrying ceremonies at the Olympic Games, or the undying flames that burn at some shrines, to see that a vestige of the magical aspect is still with us.

WHAT IS FLAME?

The chemistry textbook, of course, will tell us that flame is a chemical reaction between gases which takes place with sufficient release of energy to give rise to light and heat. Most usually, one of the reacting substances is the oxygen of the air. In most flames the other reactant is a gas also, so the flame consists of one gas mixture —air—in a rapid chemical reaction with another mixture—the fuel gas.

What do these reacting gases consist of? The air consists of nitrogen, which is chemically inert, and oxygen (the active constituent) in the ratio of $3.8 : 1$. There are some minor constituents which do not especially concern us here, such as argon (which behaves like nitrogen) and small amounts of carbon dioxide, between 0.03 and 0.3 per cent, depending on the environment.

The fuel gas, however, can vary widely in composition. As we saw in Chapter 1, there are really four types, or 'families', of fuel gas being distributed commercially:

1. Manufactured gas (coal gas)
2. Natural gas
3. Liquefiable petroleum gases (L.P. gases)
4. L.P. gas mixed with air

All four gases will give a similar flame if the burner is designed to suit them. An expert will, however, be able to detect a gas of family 1 on an aerated burner by the sharpness of the flame inner cone; and, as we shall see, only family 1 is suitable for a non-aerated burner.

The simplest type of flame is perhaps that which occurs in a uniform mixture of the gas and air—as, for instance, the explosion in the cylinder of a car engine. There petrol vapour and air are ignited by an electric spark. The spark raises the temperature high enough to start a chemical reaction in a small sphere of the mixture, and this heats up the next layer, and so the explosion wave spreads until it reaches the walls.

Such an explosive flame can be used deliberately for generating power—as in a car engine—but it can also spread devastation when it occurs accidentally, as in a mine or factory explosion. The force generated depends on many factors, of which the volume of the enclosed space and the rigidity of the retaining walls are particularly important. The flame will travel through the mixture only if it lies within certain limits; ordinary town gas of family 1, for instance, is inflammable between 6 per cent gas plus 94 per cent air and about 33 per cent gas plus 67 per cent air. If the gas percentage is under 6 or over 33 no flame will propagate through the mixture.

STATIONARY FLAMES

While this type of combustion—producing a very sudden rise in temperature, and with it an equally sudden rise in pressure—is exceedingly valuable in providing motive power, we are more concerned in this book with the peaceable flame which sits quietly on a burner tip and gives a steady supply of heat to its surroundings.

Let us have a look at the simple laboratory bunsen burner, for this is the starting point from which a great many of the burners used in the gas industry have been developed. Fig. 27 shows a section through it. From the small hole in the injector nipple A, a thin stream of gas is projected by the pressure in the gas supply. The speed at which it issues may well be about 9000 feet per minute, and this high speed causes the jet to drag into itself some of the surrounding air. The air and gas mix together as they ascend the burner tube B; they should be well mixed by the time they reach the

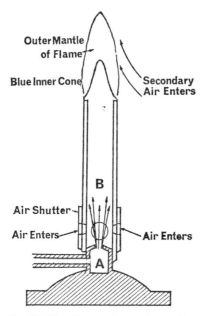

Fig. 27. The Bunsen burner in section.

burner mouth, and there should be rather more than twice as much air as gas.

At the burner mouth the chemical reaction between the fuel gas and the oxygen of the air begins, and this takes place in two stages. The first stage is exceedingly rapid. The fuel gas combines with the oxygen already mixed with it in a blue cone which forms the kernel of the flame. (We speak of a cone, but it is not often an exact geometrical cone; usually the point is rounded a little and the sides are often curved.)

If we are looking at a well-made burner, this blue cone will seem to be stationary, but what is really happening is that the flame is travelling downwards at just the same speed that the air–gas mixture is moving upwards. Looking at it another way, the flame is eating its way into the mixture; but (like a man running down an upward-moving escalator) it stays in the same place. Pinch the rubber tube quickly, and the cone will shorten—the escalator has slowed down and the man runs as fast as before. Increase the pressure of the gas and the cone lengthens—the escalator is now going faster.

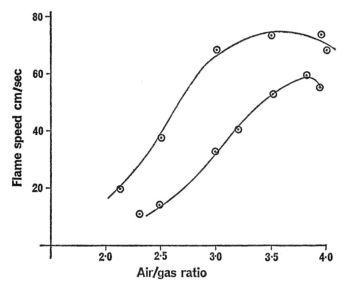

Fig. 28. Two typical curves showing the variation of flame speed with the air-gas ratio. Both these gases are conventional town gas requiring about 4·2 volumes of air for complete combustion.

We had better admit at this point that there is another complication: for the speed at which the flame-front eats its way inwards (i.e. the speed of the man running) will also vary with other factors; in particular, the composition of the original gas supply and the amount of air which has been entrained at the injector. For instance, if we are dealing with gas of family (1) (manufactured gas), the flame speed varies with the air–gas ratio somewhat as shown in the curve of Fig. 28. If the ratio is less than 2 of air to 1 of gas there is no flame propagation. Then between 2 and 3 it rapidly rises; at about 4 it reaches a maximum.

PLATE 15. A Bray jet flame.

(By courtesy of George Bray & Sons)

PLATE 16. An overhead radiant heater employing the Schwank burner principle. This unit has four burners, each of which carries eight plates of perforated refractory brick (the holes are too small to be visible in the photograph).

(By courtesy of Harris Engineering Co. Ltd.)

If we play about with the bunsen burner we can easily see the practical effect of this. The air inlet at the base has a sleeve which controls the amount of air the burner takes in. If we close this slowly, the inner cone of the flame will disappear. This indicates that the proportion of air to gas has fallen below 2, and we are in the part of the diagram where the mixture will not support flame at all. The outer flame develops a yellow plume, due to the presence of minute particles of carbon.

If we now slowly open the air shutter, the inner cone reappears and the yellow parts of the flame disappear. Now we have a rather flabby cone which is just visible; we have started to reach the beginning of the curve but because the flame speed is still low, the flame front is eating its way inwards quite slowly and we have a long inner cone.

Open the air shutter a little more, and the cone shortens quite rapidly; we are going up the steep part of the curve, and quite small increases in the proportion of air cause big increases in flame velocity. Furthermore, as we are now burning more of the gas in this first stage, less remains to be burned afterwards, and so the outer part of the flame will also have become smaller.

It may be that, if you open the air shutter fully, the cone will become so short that the burner is in danger of lighting back. Now we are getting to the upper part of the steep curve, and the flame is travelling downwards with such rapidity that the upward movement of the mixture can scarcely keep it in place. The point may come at which the flame front actually travels down the burner tube and a flame is formed at the injector. To prevent this we may have to enlarge the hole in the injector nipple, thereby increasing the upward speed of the air–gas stream. (Actually this will have a double effect; it will also reduce the air–gas ratio and so reduce the flame speed. Both effects will combine to give us a stable flame again.)

In this description we have concentrated particularly on the inner cone, which is the zone of primary combustion. The hydrocarbons in the gas are decomposed here, but hydrogen and carbon monoxide mostly burn in the outer mantle of the flame. The oxygen for this secondary stage has to come from the air around the flame, and must diffuse into it—a much slower process. In some burners used in industry all the air is introduced as primary air; then the flame

H

consists of inner cone only. This can only be achieved (as a general rule) by using gas at a higher pressure than the ordinary domestic supply.

NON-AERATED FLAMES

Some gas appliances—such as the domestic cooker—rely upon the bunsen type of burner almost entirely. In other applications, such

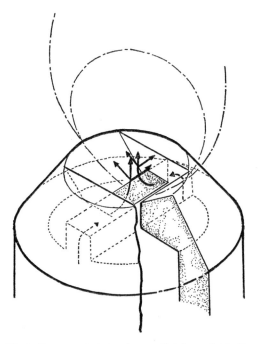

Fig. 29. A diagram showing how a flat flame jet is formed.

as water heaters and gas fires, it is more convenient to use a non-aerated burner flame, such as the one shown in Plate 15. This is a flat, fan-shaped flame, because, as we rely on secondary air entirely, we want to make it as easy as possible for the air to reach the burning gases.

The way in which this fan-shaped flame is produced is most interesting. The jets appear to be very simple in construction, and at first glance it is very difficult to see why they should give rise to a fan-shaped stream of gas. The answer is to be found in the shape of the underside of the orifice—the approach by which the gas is led up to the hole. This approach is in the form of a rectangular box, the shorter dimension of which is the same as one side of the aperture. Fig. 29 is an attempt to show how this flow pattern causes the flame to assume its characteristic shape.

The gas comes out of these jets at a speed comparable to that of the bunsen burner injector stream, and in consequence air surrounding the flame is drawn into the combustion zone very rapidly, and the gas is burned in a relatively short flame. For this reason some people prefer to call them 'non-pre-aerated' rather than 'non-aerated'; most of the air for combustion is entrained at the base of the issuing stream of gas.

CONDENSATION

Almost all fuel gases contain hydrogen, either in its elementary form or combined with carbon. (The exception is producer-gas and blast furnace gas; but these are not often used except within the industrial complex in which they are generated.) The hydrogen can only burn to form water vapour, and this is part of the products of combustion.

If one wishes to extract from the flame every vestige of heat that is generated, one must condense the water formed. The latent heat of condensation which is thereby obtained increases the heat furnished by the flame (with manufactured town gas) by about 10 per cent. While this is a very useful amount, it is usually found that the trouble and expense of disposing of the water is considerable. Nearly always it is better to prevent the water from condensing, by employing sufficient excess air in the combustion space to carry it away as vapour.

If the products of combustion, carrying the mixture as water vapour, escape into the room the water may still condense on cool surfaces—windows, walls, etc. This is one of the chief reasons why the use of unflued gas appliances for room heating is a little unsatisfactory. The use of flueless gas appliances for heating churches and halls, though at one time popular because of the economy of the system, is now largely discredited. The reason is that condensation on cold walls (and especially, in churches, on organ pipes and mechanism) can cause great damage and more than outweigh the money saved.[1]

CALORIFIC VALUE

This missing 10 per cent gives rise to some difficulty when one attempts to define the heating power (calorific value) of a gas. Conventional manufactured gas (family No. 1) usually has a total heating power of about 50 Btu/cu. ft, or 450 kcal/cu. m. This is measured in a special calorimeter designed to extract every possible scrap of heat, and nearly all the water formed is condensed in it.

In a practical gas appliance—without condensation—one cannot possibly reach this figure, and about 90 per cent is then to be regarded as the theoretical maximum. In some countries this difficulty is solved by making use of a lower figure, the net calorific value, which is the total amount of heat that can be generated by combustion, minus that portion which is attributable to condensation. In Britain, however, the gross calorific value (the higher figure) is always used, and in consequence a figure of about 90 per cent is the theoretical maximum for most appliances.

TABLE 2. Calorific value of common gases

		Btu/cu. ft		Kcal/cu. m gross
		gross	net	
Carbon monoxide	CO	318	318	3,020
Hydrogen	H_2	320	270	3,050
Methane	CH_4	996	895	9,520
Ethane	C_2H_6	1,730	1,580	16,820
Ethylene	C_2H_4	1,560	1,460	15,290

(for Propane and Butane see Table 1, Chapter 3)

The calorific values of the common constituents of fuel gases are given below in Table 2. Hydrogen and carbon monoxide both have a low calorific value (just over 300 Btu/cu. ft), whereas all the hydro-carbons are high—from about 1000 Btu/cu. ft upwards, increasing

[1] A part of the heat requirements (say 50 per cent) can, however, be met by unflued heaters in temperate climates without this trouble arising.

with molecular weight. Conventional manufactured gas, at 500 Btu, is made up of lean gases (H_2 and CO), rich gases (hydrocarbons) and inerts (nitrogen, carbon dioxide). Natural gas consists largely of methane, and consequently it has about double the calorific value of manufactured gas.

BAD COMBUSTION

With a normal gas flame the products of combustion are simply carbon dioxide, nitrogen, and water vapour. In unfavourable circumstances, however, carbon (soot) can be formed, and also carbon monoxide.

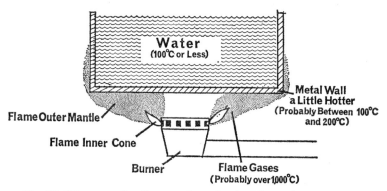

Fig. 30. Diagram of a flame under a kettle. The main temperature difference is that between the hot gases and the metal wall.

A flame burning properly on a supply of purified gas should have no smell. If it has any odour at all, combustion is probably incomplete, and some of the carbon in the combustion products is in the form of carbon monoxide instead of carbon dioxide. This can be serious, because whereas the *di*oxide is harmless (we have about 7 per cent in our lungs), the *mon*oxide is poisonous and can have serious effects on the functioning of the blood, if inhaled (see Chapter 6).

The testing of the combustion products to measure the ratio of CO to CO_2 forms a very important part of the laboratory examination of a gas appliance. In many cases this test is carried out not only under normal working conditions, but also at increased pressure and with a vitiated air supply. It is well known that some gas appliances function perfectly well when fresh clean air is fed to them, but may be less satisfactory if they are being used in a room where the oxygen content has been reduced because ventilation is inadequate.

HEAT TRANSFER FROM FLAMES

The object of burning gas is (nearly always) to produce heat, to raise the temperature of something. The flame produces a stream of very hot gases, and this heat has to be transferred, usually to a solid surface. The subject of heat transfer is material for a book by itself, and all we can do here is to indicate some of the main factors.

Consider a gas flame under a kettle: clearly, the hot gases have to impart heat to the metal wall, and this in turn heats the water. The first important fact is that an overwhelming proportion of the resistance to heat flow is at the gas–solid interface; once the heat has reached the metal it passes through to the water very easily.

The hot gases of the flame passing over the bottom of the kettle may flow smoothly over the surface; in that case there will be a slow-moving layer on the kettle bottom, and all the heat that reaches the metal wall will have to be conducted through this nearly stationary film of gas. Gases in general are poor conductors of heat, and so the rate at which heat passes depends very much on how thin one can make this stationary film.

If our burners blow on to the kettle bottom at a high speed, the dead film will be reduced. If you double the speed of the gases you will nearly double the rate of heat transfer. Also, anything you can do to create turbulence will assist heat transfer; for turbulence sweeps away some of the static layer. Fins or studs on the under surface of the kettle will help to do this. They will also increase the area of the metal surface, and this will in turn also assist heat transfer. These principles are used in the design of many gas burning appliances.

It is not enough, evidently, to generate heat by making a flame; we have also to use this heat. To persuade the heat to travel into the object (or fluid) to be heated may call for just as much science and skill as did the formation of the flame in the first place.

Prometheus—who began this chapter—has clearly left us with plenty of problems to be solved if we are to make full use of the gift of fire.

9 | Gas in the Home

Gas is made to be burned. After all the stages we have described in Chapters 2 to 6—manufacture, extraction from the earth, purification, storage, distribution—at the end of all this, it is consumed by fire, and vanishes instantly. However, just at the point where it vanishes, heat is produced, and it is the generation of heat just at the place where it is needed which is the whole purpose and justification of the gas industry.

About half the heat liberated by gas flames in Britain goes into domestic uses. The other half heats offices and factories, and in them provides the power for furnaces, ovens, boilers, air heaters, and many other appliances. This chapter will deal with the domestic uses.

COOKING

The use of gas for cooking began around the middle of the nineteenth century. At that time the chief application of gas was to lighting, and the normal way of cooking was by means of a coal or wood fire. Naturally, the first gas oven was very like a coal oven, except for the gas flame or flames in the bottom.

Today the gas cooker has become almost a standard article of household equipment, and although the electric cooker has made great strides forward, gas is still used by most homes in preference to it. It usually consists of three independent sections, mounted together for convenience:

Oven
Hotplate
Grill

and a great deal of thought and study has gone into the design of each of these parts.

Consider first the oven. Gas ovens in Britain are normally heated by one or two rod-shaped burners mounted inside and at the bottom.

The hot gases from the flame circulate around the food being cooked and then pass out, usually by a duct which terminates at the back of the hotplate. One might think that the products of combustion should be separated from the food, and it is quite possible to make an oven which is indirectly heated—i.e., the hot products of combustion pass around the outside of the oven wall and do not enter it.

Such indirectly heated ovens have not proved popular in Britain, though they are much used on the continent of Europe. They give a more uniform heat—the top and the bottom are nearly the same temperature—and whether this is desirable depends very much on the traditions of the cook. British people seem to prefer an oven which has such a difference in temperature between top and bottom that a joint of meat can be roasted near the top while a rice pudding is being cooked (at a much lower temperature) on the bottom shelf.

The effect on the flavour of the food is also different. A British direct-fired oven causes quite a high-velocity stream of hot gases to pass over the food. Some of the heat imparted to it comes from this convective effect; the remainder by radiation from the oven walls. A non-ventilated indirect-fired oven becomes filled with steam and cooks the food rather differently.

We have been discussing uniformity of heating, but of course uniformity in a horizontal plane is very necessary whatever the type of oven. Indeed, much care and trouble is taken, when a gas oven is being designed, to ensure that a tray of scones is evenly browned all round the tray and that the top and bottom of each scone will reach the same tint. This is one of the early tests; after this degree of uniformity has been attained other cooking tests follow, such as fruit cake, apple tart, and eventually a complete dinner with roast meat, potatoes, Yorkshire pudding, and a rice pudding.

The cooking of food is essentially a heating-up process, but the flavour of the end product depends a good deal on such factors as the rate of heating, the proportion of convected heat to radiant heat, and also on the way this ratio varies during the cooking period. In spite of some very interesting attempts to make a scientific analysis of the problem, the design of cookers is still a largely empirical process, and actual cookery plays a big part in the testing of any prototype.

During the 1930s the use of thermostats became general, and these represented a great advance in oven design. A heat-sensitive element in the top of the oven controls the rate of gas flow. According to the position to which the control knob is set, so the maximum temperature which the oven can reach is limited; when the limiting temperature is approached the gas valve begins to close.

The heat-sensitive element used at first was a rod of one metal inside a tube made of another material. At the far end the two were joined, and so the difference in the rate of thermal expansion caused the free end of the rod to change its position relative to the end of the tube as the temperature rose. This relative movement is enough to open or close a gas valve, and a screw plunger varies the valve

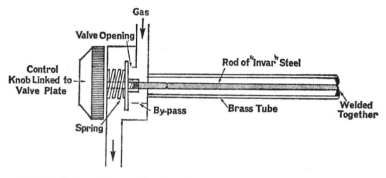

Fig. 31. A simple form of cooker thermostat. Invar steel has a very low coefficient of expansion. The effect of a rise in temperature is that the brass tube expands and the spring is able to push the valve into the closed position. The control knob makes it possible to alter the temperature at which the closing of the valve takes place. The by-pass orifice keeps the burners alight when the thermostat closes.

gap and thereby changes the temperature at which it will close. It must not close completely, of course; otherwise, a sudden turn-down of the thermostat would put the flame right out.

More recently the capsule-type thermostat has been used a great deal; this depends on the expansion of a liquid contained in a metal phial and joined to the control valve by means of a capillary tube. In both types, the thermostat is normally calibrated in arbitrary numbers; the intention is that the housewife shall learn by experience (or from the cooking chart) that No. 7 is right for roasting beef, No. 2 for rich fruit cake, and so on. Table 3 gives the approximate temperatures.

TABLE 3

Thermostat number	Type of cooking	Approx. temperature at centre of oven °F	General description
$\frac{1}{4}$	fruit bottling	240	
$\frac{1}{2}$	stews	265	very cool
1	custard and egg dishes, milk puddings	290	
2	rich fruit cake	310	cool
3	slow roasting, shortbread making	335	warm
4	madeira and plain fruit cake, biscuits	355	moderate
5	queen cakes, sponges	380	
6	plain buns, plate tarts, short pastry	400	fairly hot
7	quick roasting of meat, scones	425	hot
8	flaky pastry	445	
9	puff pastry	470	very hot

THE HOTPLATE

Above the oven is normally a hotplate, comprising three or four burners which fire upwards to the underside of cooking vessels placed above them. The design of these burners and of the pan supports which are situated above and around them is quite a delicate exercise in which conflicting requirements must be reconciled.

The designer of a hotplate burner tries to ensure that:

(a) The food is heated evenly.

(b) The heat is imparted to the vessel efficiently—i.e., with the minimum wastage of heat.

(c) The flame is stable, whether full on, or turned to the simmering position.

(d) The cooking vessel is stable and will not tip easily.

(e) Combustion of the gas is complete under all likely conditions.

(f) Any food which spills or boils over will not burn on to a hot surface so that it is difficult to remove.

(g) Any food boiling over will not interfere with the operation of the burner.

(h) The burner is stable on a wide variety of gases, will ignite easily, and will never flash back.

Some of these requirements are not easy to reconcile. For example, requirements (*b*) and (*e*) lead to the design of very thin and widely separated pan supports. However, such an arrangement is hardly likely to lead to the maximum stability of cooking vessels, requirement (*d*). The tipping-up of a saucepan can lead to a wastage of food which far exceeds in actual monetary value any saving due to increased thermal efficiency in the burner. The cost of a lost half-pint of milk is considerably greater than that of an hour's fuel consumption on a boiling burner.

One requirement we have not listed above is a good appearance. The cooker manufacturers make their product as handsome as possible, to attract the potential purchaser. At one time this was done by hiding the burners as far as possible, by covering them with sheets of enamelled steel. This produced a solid-top effect not unlike that of an electric cooker. Unfortunately it also produced a cooker hotplate which soon became very difficult to clean. The best enamelled surface is hard to cope with after milk or sugar has been left to char upon it. If spilt food falls on to a hot surface, and one which cannot easily be wiped, it usually stays there and forms a hard carbonaceous deposit which is very hard to remove.

For this reason requirement (*f*) was inserted in the above list. Some modern cookers are so designed that any food which is spilt falls on to a cool surface. It can then be wiped off after cooking operations are over. Much attention has been given to the quality of the enamel. This is a vitreous enamel—i.e., it is a film of glass-like material which is melted on to the steel in a furnace. In order to cope with fruit juices and vinegar, the enamel must be acid-resistant; it must also be as resistant as possible to mechanical damage when struck with a metal object.

Requirement (*e*)—that complete combustion shall take place—is highly important, especially as it is not normally practicable to fit a flue to a gas cooker, and the products of combustion must pass directly into the room. The problem is complicated, too, by the fact that the designer has no control over what kind of vessel is to be placed on top; the housewife may use one egg-saucepan or a couple of buckets, according to the need of the moment. Whatever she uses, the hot products of combustion must be able to pass away freely so that air may flow into the combustion zone below unhindered.

These considerations indicate how difficult a task faces the designer of a gas cooker hotplate; it is really quite surprising that the cookers available today give such excellent results. The thermal efficiency is not very high; it is normally in the region of 50 per cent. That it is no higher is due primarily to the fact that the heat-receiving surface is not designed by the cooker manufacturer; it is chosen by the housewife for a variety of reasons quite unconnected with thermal efficiency.

The surface available for heat transfer when a saucepan is placed on a gas burner is very limited. By fitting ribs or studs to the base the thermal efficiency can be increased considerably, for this enlarges the superficial area of the metal. Cooking vessels made in this way can be obtained, but most users do not seem to think the advantages repay the inconvenience or the extra cost.

Of paramount importance in these matters is the speed of the operation. Most people want their kettle to boil as quickly as possible, even though this may entail some loss in efficiency. This is a factor which the designers must take into account. The thermal efficiency could be raised considerably by a lowering of the heat input.

THE GRILLER

In Britain, cookers are nearly always fitted with a griller, which is able to send radiant heat down on to the surface of a slice of meat, bread, fish, or other food. On the continent of Europe grillers are not normally fitted, although on some cookers they are available as an extra. This, again, is a reflection of food habits in the different countries. In France it is quite common for a griller to be fitted in the top of the oven, the design being so arranged that this burner cannot be turned on if the oven burner (at the bottom) is alight.

The effect of a griller depends, however, on the fact that the food is not in a hot atmosphere; quite cold air surrounds it as the heat rays strike the outside and heat the surface layers. A griller in an enclosed space (such as an oven) does not have quite the same effect, or give quite the same flavour.

Until about 1960 the normal place for a griller was below the hotplate and above the oven. Since that time there has been an increasing tendency for it to be mounted above the hotplate—the so-called eye-level griller. This change has one or two big advantages. It enables the oven to be raised, while still keeping the hotplate at the most convenient height. The food being grilled can be seen much more easily, without bending. The griller is no longer in a position where spilt food can collect on it, as could happen rather easily in the old design. Among the cookers shown in the 1964 Approved Appliances List, high-level grillers outnumbered the low-level types by about two to one.

The griller itself consists usually of a 'grill fret' made from heat-resisting steel, and usually corrugated, perforated, or both, to increase the heat transfer rate. Flames from an aerated burner are arranged to play on the under surface so that it becomes red-hot. Either a single bar burner, with grill frets on either side, is used, or a U-shaped burner with flames playing inwards on to a larger grill fret.

WATER HEATING

The water heater has much in common with the cooker hotplate burner—and in practice the cooker hotplate is one source of hot water, using a kettle. However, the designer of an appliance for the special task of water heating can aim at a far higher thermal efficiency, because he is able to design both the burner and the heat receiving surface. Moreover, efficiency is now a matter of considerable practical importance, for the amount of energy needed to provide one hot bath is about the same as that needed to cook a dinner for several persons.

The design of a water heater makes an excellent exercise in the technology of heat transfer (which was discussed in Chapter 8). An intense heat is developed in the gas flames, and this heats up the stream of air which flows into and around them. Consequently a column of very hot gas rises up from each flame, and the problem is how best to extract heat from this column of gas and make it to pass through a dividing wall of metal into the water which is flowing on the other side of the wall.

Generally speaking, the problem usually resolves itself into the provision of sufficient heat transfer area. As we saw in Chapter 8, all the resistance to heat flow occurs between the hot gases and the cold metal wall; the resistance of the metal wall itself, and the passage of heat from it to the water, is negligible by comparison. Consequently, the conditions must concentrate on enabling the heat to flow from the gases to the metal boundary surface.

Although there are several factors influencing this rate of heat flow—such as, for instance, temperature differences, and speed of flow of the gas, much the most easily controlled factor is the total surface area. If a plain tube is fitted with fins or grills, or a flat surface is provided with studs, the advantage which accrues can be largely accounted for by the increase in cold metal surface. Fins can

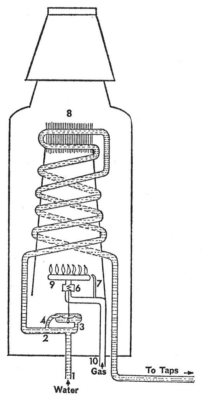

Fig. 32. A well-known type of multipoint water heater.

be arranged to increase the area of a tube by ten times, or more, and if this is done the rate of heat transfer goes up proportionately.

One form of water heater, designed to operate on a continuous flow of water (and designated 'instantaneous water heater' in the trade—although it is certainly *not* instantaneous) is shown in Fig. 32. Here there are two sets of heat-transfer surfaces, the outer mantle which surrounds the combustion chamber and the finned tubes which cross it at the top. This type of appliance is fitted with a special valve whereby the water pressure on the outlet closes or opens the gas-way. When a tap is opened in some part of the house, the pressure in the water outlet falls and the gas burner lights up. The gas flames begin to heat the water, and after a short time the outlet water flows hot. As soon as the flow of water is stopped the pressure returns to its previous value, the gas flow is thereby stopped, and the appliance comes to rest.

This type of appliance is also known as a multipoint water heater —a more sensible title than 'instantaneous'—and it is widely used to provide household hot water for bath, sink, and wash-hand basin. It burns gas at a rapid rate, because this is essential if all the heat needed for a hot bath is to be provided in (say) 8 to 10 minutes. The usual rate of heat input is about 1 therm per hour, and the output is $1\frac{1}{2}$ gallons per minute at a temperature of 80°F (45°C) above that of the inlet water.

An alternative way of providing hot water is by a storage system. This uses gas at a slower rate, but builds up a stock of hot water in an insulated tank, so that, when the bath tap is turned on, a much faster flow can be obtained. While this has many advantages, it tends to be rather less economical, because the water must be maintained at full temperature for long stretches of time when it is not required—for instance, when the household is asleep.

Another disadvantage of the storage heater is that (unless a large model is used) one cannot usually take two baths in rapid succession. However, some models have a rapid recovery rate, and this largely overcomes the difficulty.

The storage heater is essentially a small instantaneous heater combined with a hot water tank. Sometimes one can use an existing water tank and attach to it a small water heater known as a circulator. This takes cool water from the bottom of the tank, feeds it back to the top as hot water, and continues to do this until the thermostat senses that no more heat is needed, and then shuts down the gas supply.

Another variety of gas water heater is that used to supply water for central heating installations; at this stage it becomes a 'boiler' in trade parlance (although there would be grave trouble if it ever started to boil!) Central heating boilers have usually a smaller heat input than the multipoint heater, but are made of more robust construction as they are usually used for very much longer periods of time.

Most of the central heating boilers now in use are of cast-iron construction, somewhat as shown in Fig. 33. Some newer designs employ a more sophisticated heat transfer system, however. One can use a sheet steel plate to which short copper rods have been

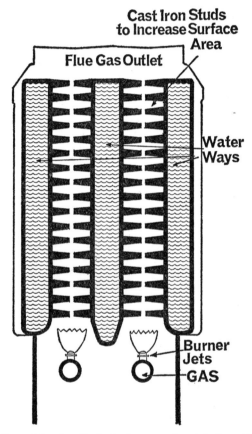

Fig. 33. Central heating 'boiler' of conventional design. (*By courtesy of Thomas Potterton Ltd.*)

welded. Copper is an excellent conductor of heat, and so one can obtain a much larger effective heating surface, and this in turn enables the size of the whole unit to be reduced.

The burners are (in Britain) nearly always of the non-aerated flat-flame type, but in countries where natural gas is used an aerated burner must be employed. Such a slow-burning gas as methane could not be retained on the flat-flame jets which are so successfully used with coal gas. In countries where a changeover to natural gas seems likely in the near future, a burner must be fitted which will operate successfully on both types of gas—a so-called all-gas burner (see Chapter 12).

A thermostat is normally fitted which will control the circulating water to the desired maximum temperature—about 160°F (70°C) is commonly used. Another, and quite independent, thermostat will probably be fitted with its sensing element in the principal living room; this serves to close down the heating system when the room is warm enough. Commonly it affects, not the gas supply directly, but the pump which drives the water round the heating circuit, through the house and back again to the boiler. By stopping the pump, it soon stops the gas too, because the water gets too hot and then the first thermostat comes into play.

One of the main problems confronting the designer of water heaters is that of corrosion. As we saw in Chapter 6, most town gas originating in coal contains traces of organic sulphur compounds, which are not removed by the conventional purifying process. The amount present depends on the sulphur content of the coal, and also on the carbonization methods. Britain is particularly unfortunate in this respect—statistics produced by the International Gas Union in 1964 showed the sulphur content of British gas to be 340 mg/cu. m, whereas Germany and Switzerland had only 200 and most other countries less still.

Sulphur compounds in the gas burn to form sulphur oxides in the flame. There are two oxides of sulphur: the dioxide SO_2 and the trioxide SO_3 (which with water forms sulphuric acid). When hot products of combustion strike a cold metal surface, some water condenses as a film on it. This will occur every time a water heater starts up from cold, but as the apparatus warms up, and the water on the other side of the metal wall becomes hotter, the film of water evaporates.

If this film of water contains even a trace of sulphuric acid, the effect of evaporating it is to concentrate the acid, driving off water first until a tiny drop of quite strong acid is left; ultimately this too will evaporate, but only after dissolving a little of the metal away. This process repeated many times a day can cause quite severe corrosion to copper, and a pale green deposit of copper sulphate is only too familiar a sight on such appliances.

This problem is, of course, being tackled, and tackled resolutely. In the first place the sulphur content of the gas is being reduced, and the moves which are taking place in the direction of detoxification are also tending to lower or even eliminate organic sulphur. It will be many years, however, before this can spread to all the gas supplied, and meanwhile improvements are envisaged on the appliance.

Aluminium has been found to be much less subject to this kind of corrosion than copper, and attempts to protect the copper surface by plating or painting have met with little success. Unfortunately aluminium is not so good on the water side; it suffers more from water corrosion than copper or brass. One possibility is that a composite heat exchanger may be used, aluminium on the outside and copper within. Both vitreous enamel and (for higher temperatures) heat-resisting alloy steel are also used successfully.

ROOM HEATING

Gas can be used to heat the rooms in your house either by using individual units in each room or by means of a centrally fired installation. In the latter case, it can spread the heat through the house either by circulating hot water (which we have already touched upon) or by blowing hot air through ducts—a method suited best to new houses.

Let us consider first the individual unit; this is based on the traditional way of heating houses by solid fuel. In Britain the open coal or wood fire was the usual method; this has led to the gas fire which was at first designed to give only radiant heat—it was supposed to warm the occupants like the sun, shining perhaps on a cold day.

On the European continent the closed stove was the traditional method of heating—a solid construction, covered with tiles, which warmed the air but did not give much radiant heat. It is not surprising that on the Continent the typical gas-fired heating unit for the individual room is the gas convector.

Since the middle 1950s the two types of unit have been moving closer. British gas appliance designers discovered (rather belatedly)[1]

[1] The practical advantage of combining a flow of warm air with radiant heat were well known before the Second World War. Yet D. R. Wills, writing in 1953, could say: "The appliance which should receive serious

that if a warm-air component was added to the radiant heat it greatly improved the comfort of the room's occupants; it also enlarged the usable area in the room (previously one had to sit round the fire to keep warm) and the speed of heating-up. Moreover, such a convector gas fire could be made to have a much higher thermal efficiency than the older type.

The process of making the people who are occupying a room warm and comfortable is one which can be analysed into physical factors. The human body is so made that it must always be giving off heat. It must lose heat to live, but for comfort it should not lose heat too slowly or too rapidly. To wear clothing is the obvious first way to reduce the rate of heat loss, but, of course, if clothes are too bulky they impede our movements. We therefore modify our climate artificially so as to ensure that the body loses heat at about the right rate when we are wearing normal light clothing.

In Britain and most other European countries people feel comfortable when the air temperature is about 65°F (18°C), but in the United States and Canada, where people are accustomed to wear lighter clothing indoors, 70°F (21°C) or even more is thought desirable. In either case, these temperatures of the air are modified if the person is exposed to radiant heat, or to a cold nearby surface.

At winter sports one can feel warm standing still, in bright sunshine, even though the air temperature is well below freezing point. Heat loss due to air temperature is being counteracted by heat absorption from the sun's rays. If you stand still too long, however, you will find yourself getting chilly on the side which is not being warmed by the sun. This is one of the disadvantages of relying too much on radiant heat. When the gas undertakings of Britain coined the phrase 'wrap-round heat' to boost their convector fires they were expressing this point very neatly. By adding warm air heating to radiant heating less radiation is needed, and a more uniform effect is produced.

On the other hand, a certain amount of unevenness is perhaps stimulating, and for this reason many people prefer a heating system

---

attention is the convector fire. Development in this direction has been desultory . . . the direct air warming by the 12 to 15 per cent added convection heat must lead to a quicker attainment of comfort." At that time hardly any convector gas fires were sold; in 1963–64 the figure approached three quarters of a million, and was still increasing.

which contains an element of radiation, as against those systems of central heating which employ little or none, and rely entirely on air temperature.

Perhaps it is partly for this reason that the convector gas fire is so popular. A section through a typical model is shown in Fig. 34.

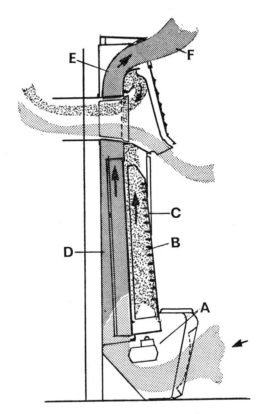

Fig. 34. Section through a convector gas fire. (*By courtesy of Cannon Gas Appliances Ltd.*)

A row of flat flames at A heats the combustion chamber, which is a flat tapering compartment formed by the firebrick back B and the row of fire-proof rods C. The inside of this compartment becomes red-hot, and radiant heat is emitted between the rods. At the same time a current of room air, drawn in at the base, is passing through D, behind the combustion chamber, where it absorbs heat. It absorbs more heat at E, where it takes it from the hot gases which are about to go up the flue. At F the warmed air emerges and flows into the room.

In some new designs a glass plate is interposed in front of the fire. This has the function of stopping air from being drawn up out of the room to dilute the combustion gases, and so the thermal efficiency is still further increased.

CENTRAL HEATING

Up till quite recently, the words 'central heating' always meant the heating of the various rooms of a building by a circulating current of hot water or steam. Hot water is the usual choice, and of recent years it has been forced round its circuit by an electric pump; this enables a much smaller-bore tube to be used, and also makes the response much quicker.

The 'boilers' were discussed in an earlier section of this chapter. The hot water gives up its heat to the air of the room by means of a system of heat exchangers commonly (and rather misleadingly) referred to as radiators. From the early cast-iron loops which were rather clumsy, the industry has moved to pressed steel units, and to gilled tubing carried inside a convector box. Sometimes this box is prolonged along the skirting board of the room, giving a very even distribution of heat. Sometimes an electric fan is incorporated, which makes it possible to get a much bigger heat output from a given size of unit.

The form of central heating which has been making the most rapid headway of recent years is the warm-air system. This central unit heats not water, but air; the warm air is circulated through the house. In the more expensive installation this is done by ducts, but many flats today are heated by a selective air heater which discharges warm air directly into either kitchen, living room, or hall. Shutters can be opened or closed to drive the warm air in the direction of those parts of the house where warmth is needed at the moment.

Some idea of the progress made by warm-air systems in Britain is given by figures published by The Gas Council which show the number of new installations:

	Warm air	Central heating boilers
1958–59 . .	1,000	2,500
1959–60 . .	3,000	10,000
1960–61 . .	8,000	18,000
1961–62 . .	15,000	22,000
1962–63 . .	21,000	35,000
1963–64 . .	30,000	60,000

While this is partly an indication of increasing prosperity and growing ability to provide comfort in the home, it also shows how rapidly the popularity of both systems is growing.

Most warm-air systems are installed in new housing projects. The flow of air obviously requires a conduit of far larger cross-section than is needed for the flow of hot water, and it may be difficult and expensive to install warm air systems in an existing building. On the other hand, if one starts before a new building is erected, warm air circulation is cheaper in first cost, more rapid in operation, and more flexible in use. There is nothing to freeze up if the house is left unoccupied in cold weather; there are no water valves to leak, and no expansion tanks in the roof.

In a warm-air heater, gas is normally burned in a metal chamber or series of chambers, while air is blown over the outside of the chamber walls by a fan. It is rather easier to construct such an appliance with air travelling upwards, but there are practical advantages in making the air flow downwards so that it can be emitted into the room just above floor level. The products of combustion are carried away by an ordinary flue or chimney.

In such a down-flow heater the air will normally be drawn in from grilles placed near the ceiling. This system has another advantage, for it reduces the dust deposition on the ceiling which tends to occur if warm air is emitted at a high level. Warm air tends to rise, and careful tests have shown that a more even distribution of temperature is obtained when the warm air is blown into the room at low level and taken out at high level.

The position of the return air grille exercises an important influence on the pattern of air circulation. In a large and lofty room, for instance, it may be preferable to withdraw the return air at low level, and as far as possible from the inlet grille; this would tend to draw the air down and prevent it from forming a warm static layer near the ceiling.

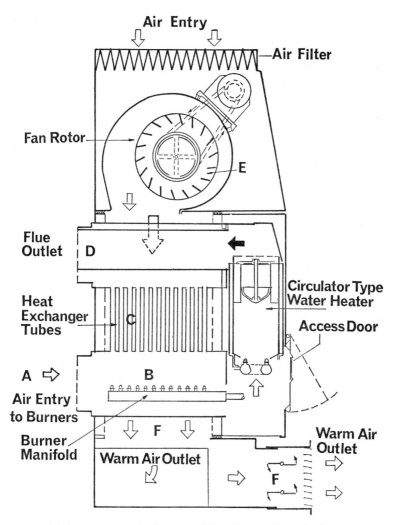

Fig. 35. A warm air unit for a small flat, The air from the fan passes behind the flueway D and flows forwards through the heat exchanger tubes C to the warm air box at F. A circulator type water heater is built into the appliance in this particular example. (*By courtesy of William Sugg & Co. Ltd.*)

A typical warm air unit is shown in Fig. 35. Air for combustion enters at A and passes to the combustion chamber B. The hot products of combustion give their heat to the metal walls C, which are also heated to some extent by direct radiation from the flame. The cooled, burned gases pass out through the flue D. A current of air is blown over the outer surface of the metal walls by a fan E and passes to the outlet duct F.

While very good results can be obtained in small apartments by discharging the warm air straight from the unit directly into the room, more elaborate installations with extended ductwork give a more uniform heating. The principle of peripheral heating was introduced in the United States. In this system the warm air is discharged round the periphery of the living space—i.e., on the inside of the outer walls—and it necessitates ducts under the floor. The return air flows back into the heater at a more or less central gathering point.

'COLD RADIATION'

While discussing house warming one should refer to the effect of large cold surfaces, which can be said (speaking very loosely) to 'radiate coldness'. In physical terms, this means that the body of the occupant is radiating heat to a cold surface—a surface which cannot radiate back in return as would a warm wall. The effect is that the person feels chilled on the side facing towards the cold surface.

Such a cold surface is usually a glass window, for glass conducts heat much more readily than other parts of the building. Modern structures embodying large areas of plate glass exhibit this phenomenon in quite a striking fashion. Double glazing reduces the heat loss through a window greatly, but this is an expensive and rather inconvenient expedient. Heavy curtains usually solve the problem at night time, but during the day time it will usually be necessary to work to a higher air temperature to compensate for 'cold radiation'. This is doubtless one of the reasons for the advantages claimed for the peripheral heating system referred to above. A similar effect is obtained with hot-water central heating by using skirting-board convector strips.

DUST DEPOSITION ON COLD SURFACES

If a stream of warm air flows over a surface which is cooler than itself, dust particles suspended in the stream are forced on to the cold surface. This is a particularly embarrassing phenomenon, and has caused much distress among householders who have installed central heating in newly decorated houses.

This physical phenomenon is nothing to do with gas fuels, of course; the ceiling above an electric light bulb becomes darkened in just the same fashion. It is more noticeable in urban areas than in country districts, but even in remote parts of the country, where there is very little soot in the air, household dust collects and this can be carried up in a warm air stream.

The practical answer is to ensure that warm air streams do not, as far as possible, come immediately into contact with walls or ceilings. Hot water radiators or convector heaters should not produce a column of warm air rising vertically, but should be designed to throw the air stream forward. (The convector fire illustrated in Fig. 34 has been designed with this aspect specially in mind.) Water radiators are often placed under windows; only the curtains then become soiled, and they are more easily washed than a wall.

REFRIGERATION

All refrigerating units depend for their cooling effect upon the fact that, when a liquid evaporates, heat is absorbed. This is a phenomenon we are all familiar with; the heat of a gas burner turns boiling water into steam, and this can go on for a long while without the temperature of the water rising; all the heat is going into the vaporization process. If you hold your wet hand in a fast current of air the skin becomes very cold, because the water is evaporating and taking heat from your hand.

Many electrical refrigerators employ a volatile liquid which travels round a cycle in which there are abrupt changes in pressure. At the entrance to the cooling unit the liquid passes through an orifice into a region of much lower pressure; there it evaporates, taking up heat from its surroundings as it does so. The gas circulates in the cold box and then passes out to a pump which re-compresses it, causing it to condense to liquid form again. This condensation is accompanied by the release of heat. (Fig. 36A.)

This heat must be dissipated, cooling the liquid down to room temperature, before the cycle is repeated. Thus heat is removed from the surroundings at one point (evaporation) and is given out at another (condensation). If the evaporation unit is placed inside a

I<small>B</small>

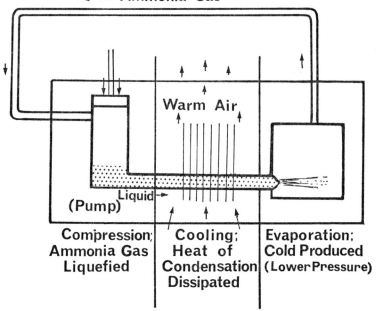

← Ammonia Gas

Warm Air

Liquid

(Pump)

| Compression; Ammonia Gas Liquefied | Cooling; Heat of Condensation Dissipated | Evaporation; Cold Produced (Lower Pressure) |

Fig. 36A. The basic principle of the refrigerator.

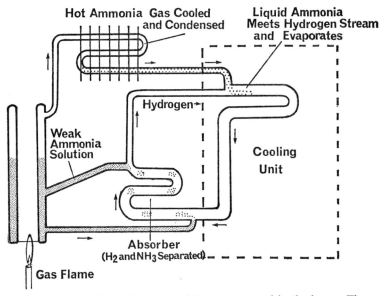

Hot Ammonia Gas Cooled and Condensed

Liquid Ammonia Meets Hydrogen Stream and Evaporates

Hydrogen →

Weak Ammonia Solution

Cooling Unit

Absorber (H_2 and NH_3 Separated)

Gas Flame

Fig. 36B. The absorption type refrigerator as used in the home. The cooling unit to the right is *inside* the insulated casing of the refrigerator, and the left-hand part of the system (which liberates heat) is *outside*.

thermally insulated box, the continual extraction of heat lowers the temperature and we have a refrigerator. (If, instead, we immerse the evaporation unit in a river and the condensation unit in a building we have a heat pump to provide warmth—but that is another story.)

In a gas refrigerator the same cycle takes place, but in place of the pump a different method is used to make it operate. The refrigerating liquid (ammonia) is made to evaporate, not by a fall in total pressure, but by the introduction of an inert gas (usually hydrogen). In one sense this effects a reduction in the pressure because, although the total pressure of the mixture is the same as before the hydrogen was added, the partial pressure (due to the ammonia alone) is necessarily reduced, and this causes evaporation.

It remains to separate the ammonia from the hydrogen after the gases have come from the cold zone, so that the cycle can continue. This is achieved by making use of the fact that ammonia is very soluble in water, and hydrogen hardly at all. Water is introduced; it rapidly seizes all the ammonia, and then, by separating liquid from gas, the hydrogen is removed. The ammonia solution is then boiled to separate the water and ammonia again, and it is a small gas flame which effects the boiling.

The ammonia gas produced contains no hydrogen and only a little water vapour; it is cooled to room temperature and is then ready to re-enter the evaporation unit. At this point the hydrogen, which has been separated off (see the previous paragraph), rejoins the liquid ammonia and again causes it to evaporate. So the cycle goes on, by day and night, continually extracting heat from the inside of the refrigerator and liberating it in the room.

The hydrogen–ammonia cycle just described is not so efficient in energy conversion as is the pumping system we mentioned first; it has, however, the big advantage of being free from any moving parts and absolutely silent. Fig. 36B illustrates the operation of the gas refrigerator.

These are the principal ways in which gas serves the householder and helps in the running of an ordinary home. There are other ways of lesser importance—such as the gas incinerator, the gas poker, the gas light. The first of these will be dealt with in Chapter 11, together with industrial incinerators. Gas lighting will also be mentioned in Chapter 11.

10 | Gas in the Factory and in Commerce

At the beginning of the last chapter we commented on the speed with which the gas, made so carefully and transported perhaps great distances, was abolished in an instant, in a flame. This process occurs on a far larger scale when we come to the factory. Here heat is needed in vast quantities, and so correspondingly large amounts of gas have to be consumed.

About half all the gas distributed in Britain goes to factories, public institutions, and commercial premises; in Germany the figure is over 80 per cent, and in the Soviet Union 90 per cent. In the latter case, however, industrial users include such voracious consumers as electric power stations, cement works, and blast furnaces. Gas is only likely to be used for these purposes when there is a really abundant supply of natural gas. Indeed, many people think this to be rather wasteful of natural resources, for such large consumers do not need such a refined fuel. In France the use of natural gas for electricity generation is declining, as better uses are found for gas in places where a high-class fuel of constant quality is necessary.

In Western Europe, gas is not usually the cheapest fuel; both oil and coal (or coke) are generally less expensive per unit of heat. Therefore gas is not usually used for such purposes as large-scale steam raising—except close to a natural gas field. The tendency is to employ gas in industry for those uses where fine control is needed and where cleanliness of operation is important—as in furnaces for the firing of pottery or metal. For instance, in the pottery industry centred around Stoke-on-Trent, in England, the old solid-fuel kilns have largely been displaced and gas is generally used. This has the advantage not only of making possible far more accurate control of the temperature, but also it prevents the smoke pollution of the atmosphere.

Some figures quoted by H. P. Lupton (*Industrial Gas Engineering*, Walter King, 1960) show what a remarkable shift has taken place in this particular industry. In the Stoke-on-Trent area the gas used for the firing of ceramics was:

1933	37 million cu. ft
1956	5000 million cu. ft
1957	6500 million cu. ft

and this may be taken as a good example of the kind of work that the gas flame is doing in industry.

In a single chapter one can only glance at the subject, for we obviously cannot cover the whole field of industrial heat processes. Let us start with one typical industrial gas application—metal melting. A pottery kiln will be described later on in this chapter.

METAL MELTING

The usual way of melting the metals of lower melting point is to place them in a pot made of iron or (at higher temperatures) one of the refractory non-metallic materials available for such purposes. It is a little similar to the domestic ring under the bottom of the kettle, but with a good many differences:

(*a*) The vessel is surrounded by refractory brickwork to reduce the heat loss.

(*b*) The burners will not normally fire directly at the pot bottom, but will probably fire into the chamber tangentially to produce a swirling mass of hot gases.

(*c*) The burners will usually be fully aerated; they will contain all the air required for combustion pre-mixed. It usually follows that the flame gases will be travelling at a much higher speed than on domestic appliances, and will be turbulent in character (for explanation of turbulent flow see page 62).

(*d*) The surface of the pot will of course become much hotter than the outside of a kettle (which cannot rise much above 100°C).

A cross-section of a lead-melting furnace is shown in Fig. 37. Of course, the amount of gas this burns is on a larger scale than is met in domestic usage. This appliance might well consume 5 therms per hour, or some forty times as much as a domestic boiling burner.

It will also give out much more noise than could be tolerated in an ordinary household, for the amount of heat released per unit volume of combustion space is far higher; and it is difficult to achieve a high intensity of heat release without noise.

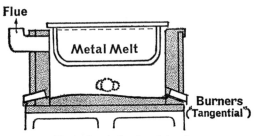

Fig. 37. A simple lead-melting furnace.

TUNNEL BURNERS

Such a furnace would usually be fired with tunnel burners of the general pattern shown in Fig. 38. Air and gas are mixed together in the proportions which will give complete combustion, and are then fed into one end of a tunnel lined with refractory firebrick. In the entry tube the mixture is moving too fast to maintain a flame, but at the point where it emerges into the tunnel there is a sudden

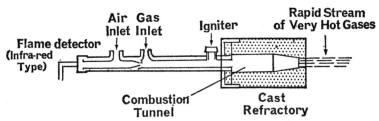

Fig. 38. A tunnel burner as might be used in the furnace in Fig. 37.

slowing-down in speed. Even more important, there are eddies formed in a ring round the mouth of the tube, and for these two reasons a stable flame is formed in the firebrick tunnel.

The inside of the tunnel, as you can imagine, rapidly becomes very hot. The firebrick walls are made of a very resistant material, and they radiate heat back on to the flame, which thereby becomes hotter still. Each rise in temperature increases the rate of combustion, and so a very large amount of gas can be burned in a small space. From the mouth of the tunnel emerges an extremely hot stream of burnt gases, travelling at a high velocity. This hot stream is a very powerful source of heating, for, as we saw in Chapter 8, the higher the velocity of a gas stream, the more rapidly does it part with its heat to a solid surface. Such a solid surface could be the outside of a metal-melting pot (as we have just seen), or it could equally be a cylindrical piece of steel which must be heated in order to be shaped (as a preliminary to drawing it out into bar or tube, for instance).

The control of a mixture of air and gas which is made before burning takes place is not without its problems (considerable care must be exercised to ensure that the flame does not run back into the pipe), and some tunnel burners are made which employ nozzle mixing—i.e., the air is admitted in a ring around the outside of the nozzle carrying the incoming gas, and the two only mix at the flame point, in the tunnel. The air is blown in from a fan, through a ring of small holes, and its momentum is enough to suck in the gas (which is maintained at a very low pressure in the nozzle).

In either system, the tunnel in which combustion occurs can be either a plain cylinder, or it can converge to an outlet which is narrower than the inlet (as shown in the drawing). Sometimes several gas and air inlets fire into a single slot-shaped tunnel. A sparking plug is generally placed in the mouth of the gas pipe, where it can ignite the flame at the beginning and not get too hot when combustion is proceeding.

CONTROL SYSTEMS

Such burners are provided with controls far more complicated than those normally used in domestic apparatus. With gas rates of this kind, and burners firing into large furnaces, it is absolutely imperative that the gas shall be ignited immediately, and that the supply shall be turned off at the moment flame ceases. Otherwise exceedingly damaging explosions could be caused.

An essential part of the equipment is a means of detecting flame. In some simple gas appliances used in the home, flame is detected by its heating effect on a compound strip of metal. In many multi-point water heaters, for instance (as described in the last chapter), a small pilot flame heats the compound strip, which is made of two metals that expand at a different rate. The strip bends when heated, and so causes a valve to open which in turn controls the main gas stream.

Although not perfect, this bimetal system works well in a water heater, where the combustion chamber is surrounded by water-cooled surfaces. It could not be used in a furnace, because the whole combustion chamber may be very hot and the brickwork will remain hot for some time after the gas has been turned off. In such industrial applications it is necessary to employ some sensing device which will detect *flame*, as distinct from *heat*.

One such device uses a photocell to detect ultra-violet light from the flame. The blue cone of a bunsen flame emits a certain amount of ultra-violet radiation, which does not occur in the glow from heated brickwork. It can be used therefore as a certain indication that flame is present. Another scheme is to use the electric conductivity of a flame; for a flame, consisting of highly ionized (charged) particles, is a much better conductor of an electric current than is hot air.

Better still is the scheme which depends on flame rectification. In this system use is made of the fact that, because the flame gases are so highly ionized, they conduct an electric current more in one direction than the other. It follows that an alternating current, applied to electrodes in a flame, is partially rectified—i.e., turned into a direct current. This is the basis of a flame-detection system which, it seems, cannot be deceived.

In a typical control system for a series of tunnel burners firing (let us say) into a large furnace, there are flame-detecting electrodes and an igniter spark or coil. The electrical circuit is arranged so that the gas can be turned on for a short period of time, and at a low rate of flow, while the igniter is sparking. After a time interval of perhaps a second has elapsed the gas valve automatically closes again unless the flame rectification system shows that a flame has been started.

PROTECTIVE ATMOSPHERES

When gas is completely burned, without any excess air, the products consist almost entirely of nitrogen, carbon dioxide, and water vapour. If not quite enough air is used, a certain amount of hydrogen and carbon monoxide will also be present in the mixture; it is then said to be a 'reducing atmosphere'. Both neutral and reducing atmospheres are widely used in the heat treatment of metals, to prevent the oxygen of the air attacking the hot metal and causing an oxide film.

This seems at first sight a strange use for gas, for the heat liberated is usually not used to the full; often indeed it is discarded completely. "Why not use nitrogen from a cylinder?" one might ask. The answer is simply that of cost. It is far more economical to use town gas as a means of generating an inert atmosphere than to use an inert gas specially made and brought to the site in cylinders.

One of the oldest and most important uses of the protective atmosphere is in the bright-annealing of copper. After copper strip has been made it must usually be put through an annealing process. It must be raised to a temperature below red-heat and kept there for a period of time depending on the thickness and other factors. This makes the metal more ductile so that it can be fashioned into the shape desired in the next stage of manufacture.

At one time the annealing process was followed by treatment with acid to remove the film of copper oxide formed while annealing. This was troublesome and also wasteful, for a not inconsiderable quantity of copper was dissolved away in the acid. Nowadays copper is bright-annealed—it is subjected to the heat treatment while surrounded by an atmosphere which contains almost no oxygen, so that the metal surface remains bright the whole time.

Protective atmospheres are also widely used in the heat treatment of steel, but in this case there is the added complication that the surface of the steel can absorb or give up carbon. In the process known as gas carburizing the atmosphere is adjusted to ensure that the surface of the steel absorbs some carbon and thereby a tough hard outer skin is formed.

THE LARGE FURNACE

Perhaps the most striking use of gas in industry is in the large high-temperature furnaces. These are usually specially designed and built for their particular purpose, so one can only hope to choose a fairly typical example by way of illustration.

Fig. 39 shows a furnace for the firing of pottery (usually called a 'kiln' in the trade) which is designed to heat nearly 2 tons of tableware to a temperature of 1230°C. The time period, from the first lighting-up to the final extraction of the ware at the end of the process, is 28 hours. This is an intermittent furnace, being heated up and cooled down again for each batch. (For large-scale mass production, a continuous process is mostly used, in which case the ware is moved very slowly through a furnace which stays hot all the time.)

The general principles can be seen from the cross-section. Before lighting up, the ware is stacked carefully on a trolley (A) which really constitutes the whole bottom of the furnace. It is pushed in

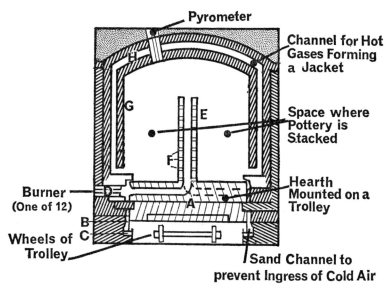

Fig. 39. Pottery kiln for the firing of tableware. (*After Lupton.*)

before firing begins, and is wheeled out again at the end of the process. A steel flange B goes into a sand trough C so that the inside is effectively sealed off from the outside air.

One of the tunnel burners is shown at D; the next one behind it would come in from the right-hand side, and so on alternately along the whole length of the structure. In this furnace the hot gases from the tunnel burner are propelled up through a duct E so that they emerge through the holes F in a series of jets impinging directly on the heaped-up ware (which of course is not shown in the diagram).

In operation the whole of the inside wall G becomes white-hot, and in order to reduce the loss of heat through this wall the flue ducts H are led behind it. In consequence, the back of the wall is only at a little lower temperature than the front, and very little heat is conducted through it. This method of jacketing the furnace with flue gases adds to the thermal efficiency considerably.

A possible additional feature—not shown here—would be a heat exchanger which would make use of some of the heat carried away by the flue gases to heat up the incoming air. This kind of furnace does not use a protective atmosphere, for this is not necessary; if, on the other hand, billets of steel were being heated some such precaution would probably be used.

INDUSTRIAL USES OF RADIANT HEAT

As the elementary physics books tell us, heat can be transmitted by three methods—conduction, convection, and radiation. The tunnel burners described earlier in this chapter give a very fast-moving stream of hot gas and so are ideal for imparting heat by convective transfer—i.e., by the movement of hot gases. However, radiation plays a very important part in nearly all industrial heating processes.

In the kind of furnace just described, for instance, the firebrick lining of the chamber is red- or white-hot, and a large amount of the heat received on the ware comes from radiation from the furnace walls.

Obviously, in a furnace, the goods to be heated are also surrounded with a hot gaseous atmosphere which is imparting heat by convective processes, and indeed special efforts are made in design to increase this effect, as we have seen. When we speak of the industrial uses of radiant heat we usually have in mind applications in which radiation is the main vehicle for heat transfer, such as the infra-red tunnel used in paint-stoving. The use of stoving enamels is one of the most valuable techniques for protecting the outside surface of metals, and particularly steel. These enamels are paints which need a certain amount of heat so that the chemical changes can occur which cause them to harden into a smooth protective coat.

Very often it is necessary to effect this surface heating of the paint as quickly as possible, and without too much heating of the metal article—as, for instance, when a soldered object has to be coated. For such purposes it is usual to use a horizontal tunnel which may be several feet in diameter and 10 or 20 feet long. A mechanical conveyor moves the painted articles through the tunnel, suspended on hooks, and the inside of the tunnel is made to radiate heat on to them.

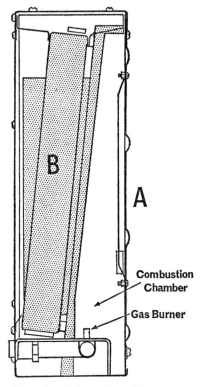

Fig. 40. Infra-red panel unit in section. (*By courtesy of Parkinson & Cowan Industrial Products Ltd.*)

The word 'infra-red' is often used to describe this system, because the radiant units mounted on the inside of the tunnel are often (but not always) below red heat. All the radiation is therefore of a longer wavelength than that of visible light. Fig. 40 shows a typical infra-red emitter panel of the type used for paint stoving. The metal plate A is heated by the gas combustion chamber behind it, and insulating bricks B on the other side of the chamber reduce the heat losses in that direction to a minimum.

THE SCHWANK BURNER

A radiant heater which is not strictly infra-red—since it glows orange-red when in operation—was invented about 1950 by the German engineer, Gunther Schwank. This makes use of a fairly thick ceramic plate perforated with thousands of small holes. The plate is made of a special low-conductivity ceramic material, having a very fine porous structure produced by the admixture of carbonaceous material with the clay before it is baked.

This property of low conductivity is essential to the working of the heater, because a tiny flame forms at the outlet of each of the perforations, and with ordinary ceramic materials the whole channel would soon get red-hot and the flames would flash back to the inside of the burner. The burner draws in all the air required for combustion at the injector, and this is only possible if the speed at which the air–gas mixture moves out through these perforations is lower than that used in an ordinary aerated burner. If the perforations were larger, the flame would soon flash back to the burner box; the combination of small-diameter hole and low-conductivity brick makes the burner stable.

It also causes the surface of the brick to become red-hot, reaching a temperature of between 850 and 900°C, and this is quite an efficient radiator of heat. The Schwank burner can be used in tunnels for the heat treatment of numerous small articles carried through on a conveyor (such as described above for stoving enamels), but it can also be used very advantageously for the heating of large and draughty working spaces.

Plate 15 shows a typical Schwank burner unit as used for heating the working spaces in a factory. Although good comfort will never be obtained if the air is really cold, draughty conditions can be ameliorated considerably by a generous supply of radiant heat from a burner of this kind. On the European Continent restaurants often use such burners to make open-air balconies attractive when the weather is cool. Large aircraft hangars, or factories in which it is frequently necessary to open large doors to the outside air, are commonly heated in this manner.

In this chapter we have touched on some of the uses of gas in industry, and have tried to give a general picture of an aspect of town gas which is not usually appreciated by the general public.

K

There is one very important use of gas with which we have not dealt: that is large-scale catering, which probably accounts for at least 10 per cent of all the gas used in the Western European countries. The appliances used, however, are basically similar to those described in the domestic uses section of this book (though larger, of course). Another quite important field is that of incinerators, but as they are used both in home and in factory, they are described in the next chapter.

11 | On Flues and Other Things

Warm air tends to rise because it is less dense than the air surrounding it. The first primitive chimney was a hole in the roof of the baronial hall. The smoke which rose up from the open wood fire curled around the rafters and then escaped through the hole. This was not a very efficient flue, because (for one thing) the smoke became mixed with so much of the surrounding air that it no longer had much buoyancy. Moreover, if all the smoke is to be evacuated it must take with it a large volume of air; a corresponding volume of cold air must be drawn into the room to replace it, and this means cold draughts whistling from every door and window. A good chimney should prevent an excess amount of air from mixing with the rising column of burned gases; then they will stay hot and rise more determinedly.

In 1796 that amazing empirical scientist, Count Rumford, showed the importance of this aspect in his study of chimney design. He demonstrated that most chimneys in his day had much too large a cross-section. By providing a quite narrow throat just above the fireplace the products of combustion remained much hotter—and the fire was less likely to smoke. (Another welcome aspect of the restriction was that it reduced the amount of air carried up the chimney, and so less cold air had to be sucked in to replace it.)

These principles are well known to the gas appliance designer, who has to ensure that the products of combustion, although they contain no smoke, must yet be carried away to the outside air. The gas cooker is one of the few gas appliances which are not usually provided with a flue, and that is largely because of the practical difficulties involved. Moreover, cooker burners are only in operation for relatively short periods, and a kitchen is usually a well-ventilated room, if only because of the need to dissipate the smell of food. Small water heaters for use over a sink or wash-hand basin also have a special dispensation, because they are normally only used for 5 minutes or so at one time. In some countries (such as Britain) small room heaters are also permitted, but with a stringent restriction on the amount of gas which may be consumed.

At the top of the flue or chimney, where it enters the free air, the pressure of the flue gases must be the same as that of the atmosphere around. Supposing the gas appliance is 10 feet below this point, the functioning of the flue depends on the difference in weight between

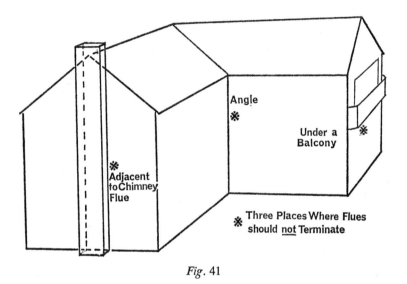

Fig. 41

a 10-foot column of flue gases at their average temperature and a column (of the same height) of the atmosphere at its average temperature. This difference results in a very small pressure difference (1/100 inch water column or less) at the base of the flue, but this is sufficient to drive the gases up it, provided that the resistance of the flue is low and air conditions outside are undisturbed.

Although this simple technique for removing products of combustion has the virtue of great simplicity, the fact that so small a force is all that is available to push the flue gases out of the appliance and into the outside air represents a considerable handicap. For example, it makes a very wide tube necessary, since the flue must have a very low resistance. Again, the movement of wind about the outside of the building creates pressure (and suction) pockets; the value of these pressures may be considerably greater than the pressure provided by the flue. In this case, if there is a positive pressure outside, air will flow down the flue and drive the flue gases down before it.

Two measures are taken to obviate the danger which might come from such a situation. In the first place, flue terminations should not be placed in parts of the building where pressure is likely to be built up by the wind. Fig. 41 shows some of these positions; a flue pipe ending here is almost certain to experience a down-draught on

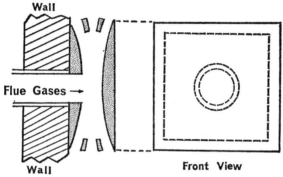

Fig. 42. Flue terminal for fitting to the face of a wall.

occasion. In a conventional house with sloping roof the ridge is a very good place; special ridge-tiles are available to end a flue in a neat and inconspicuous fashion, practically free of down-draught.

Apart from this, the flue should end either above the highest part of the roof (ideally) or at least 2 feet above the eaves (more practicable). Whilst these are the counsels of perfection, a great many gas appliances are fitted with flues that terminate on a flat vertical wall face. The flue endings (or terminals) are then so shaped that wind blowing across will tend to suck out the flue gases, on the venturi principle (see Fig. 42). The installation which is really bad is that in which the flue ends in a recess, or under an overhanging sill or balcony; then downdraught is certain to occur when the wind blows against it.

The first measure we take, therefore, is to place the end of the flue in a suitable place on the outside of the building. The second precaution is to provide a draught diverter which will ensure that, even if down-draught occurs, it will not blow into the combustion chamber. Some typical draught diverters are shown in Fig. 43. The exact dimensions are important; quite a small change will turn an efficient diverter into a very bad one. An efficient draught diverter is one which (*a*) does not spill out any flue gases when working normally, (*b*) in the event of a down-draught, vents all the flue gases

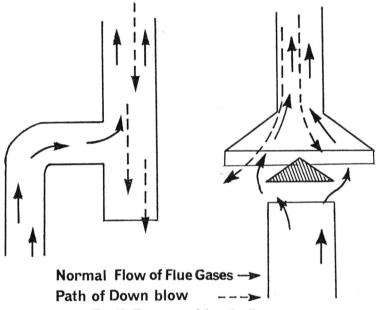

Normal Flow of Flue Gases →
Path of Down blow — — →

Fig. 43. Two types of draught diverter.

into the room and leaves the condition of the combustion chamber unaltered. The flames should be undisturbed, and the amount of air drawn in to them should be practically unaffected.

The foregoing remarks apply particularly to water heaters, but also to some commercial appliances, such as large air heaters for factories. If a draught diverter were not used, a down-draught might blow the flames right out, or if it did not do that, it might easily interfere with combustion so much as to produce large amounts of carbon monoxide which would flow into the room. In older installations the draught diverter was a separate unit, and clearly visible in the flue; more modern appliances usually have a built-in draught diverter.

NEW KINDS OF FLUE FOR BLOCKS OF FLATS

The kind of flue we have been talking about is all very well for the small house, or the building of two or three stories. When one

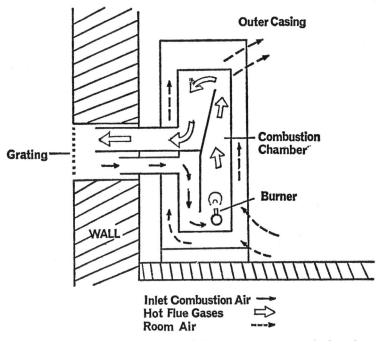

Fig. 44. Diagram of a room-sealed gas convector employing the balanced-flue principle.

comes to consider installing gas appliances in a block of flats ten, fifteen, or twenty stories high it becomes much more difficult. If all the flues run up to the top of the building, a large proportion of the upper stories will be taken up with flues which come from the lower part of the building. The system then becomes wildly extravagant in materials and in space.

One can, of course, use a single flue and let each storey feed into it; but this is generally very undesirable. Smells, noises, even products of incomplete combustion can then pass from one apartment to the other—the social consequences of this can well be imagined. Even more serious, a gas appliance left turned on but unlit could spread havoc in other dwellings using the same flue.

The solution which has been adopted has been to develop a range of room-sealed appliances. These have a combustion chamber which is sealed off from the air of the living room, drawing their air for combustion from outside the room and venting the products of combustion back in the same direction. If the appliance is fitted on an outside wall the two ducts (i.e., incoming air and outgoing flue gases) end in a special terminal so designed that wind forces affect them both equally. The appliance has its own internal circulation of incoming air and outgoing flue gases, practically unaffected by the fiercest gale that rages outside. A gas convector of this kind is shown in Fig. 44, and water heaters are made on the same principle.

However, in a large building it is not convenient to mount the gas appliances only on an outside wall, and a new system has been developed which uses a central vertical shaft running through the middle of the building from top to bottom. The idea originated in the South Eastern Gas Board, and it has been named the SE-duct. Air enters the SE-duct by means of several (usually two) horizontal ducts at ground level; these are so placed that if one opening is to windward, the other will be on the leeward side.

In a large shaft of this kind, running the whole height of the building, a very large volume of air flows upwards even if no gas appliances are in use. So great is this volume that it is quite satisfactory to let the flue gases go into it and also to draw the air for combustion from the same shaft. It is true that this incoming air is to some extent vitiated by the products of combustion of appliances on lower levels. However, in a properly designed installation the carbon dioxide in the duct will never exceed 2 per cent even with every gas appliance in use; and in practice, of course, they will never be all in use at the same time. A level of 2 per cent CO_2 does not cause malfunctioning of the appliances. Fig. 45 shows a cross-section through a building in which this system has been installed.

The SE-duct system has had a very great effect on the installation of gas appliances in new multi-storey buildings. It is safe to say that conventional flueing is out of the question in some of the tall blocks being built today, and but for this new invention gas would be little used in them. Thanks, however, to this new development, gas is very popular.

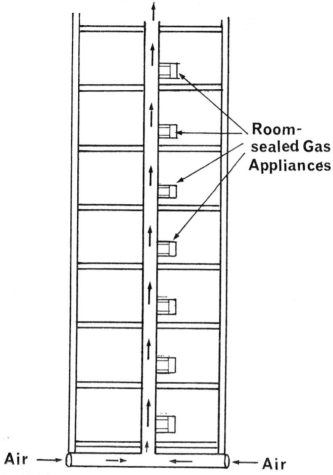

Room-
sealed Gas
Appliances

Air ⟶   ⟶   ⟵   ⟵ Air

Fig. 45. Diagram illustrating the use of room-sealed appliances in a multi-storey building, on the SE-duct principle.

INCINERATORS

As the use of solid-fuel fires and slow-combustion stoves decreases, more interest is being taken in the gas incinerator. No longer can you 'just throw it on the fire'—the only fire on the premises may be a modern convector gas fire, which is quite unsuitable for such a purpose. There is therefore an increasing demand for the domestic incinerator. In many industries also, and in hospitals particularly, it is necessary to dispose of substances which cannot be dealt with in any other way than by burning.

The materials will sometimes burn easily, and only need a minimum of heating to ignite the whole mass. More frequently they

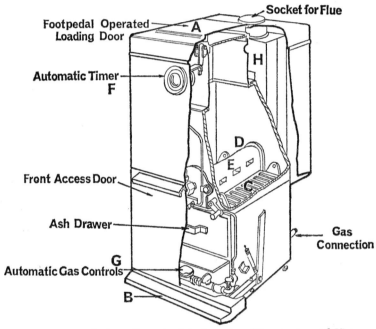

Fig. 46. A typical medium-sized incinerator. (*By courtesy of Victor Products (Wallsend) Ltd.*)

are wet and not easily burned; the problem then is to destroy them without producing smoke. More and more, in civilized countries, authorities are taking steps to prevent the emission of smoke into the air, and this is a special design consideration for the incinerator manufacturer.

To prevent smoke, it is usually necessary to install a second (empty) combustion chamber into which the burned gases pass before they go to the chimney. Here additional burners may be placed, and air inlets, so that the carbonaceous matter carried by the flue gases is oxidized. Even if this is done, a certain amount of grit may still be carried up the chimney, and (in large installations) a water spray is sometimes used to remove this.

Fig. 46 shows a medium-sized incinerator in section—this is the kind of machine which would be used in a hospital ward or a canteen kitchen; it is somewhat more elaborate than the domestic model, and has a bigger capacity. The rubbish to be consumed is inserted through the top lid, A; this is controlled by a foot pedal B, so that the person carrying the bin has both hands free. Along the centre of the grate C runs a hump D concealing the gas burners; they fire out of the windows E. This arrangement is designed to prevent the garbage from getting into the burner.

The time during which the gas burner is alight is controlled by an automatic timer, F; this controls the pressure above the diaphragm of relay valve G, by means of a thin tube not shown in the diagram (see pressure loading, page 68), and there is also incorporated a flame safety device which shuts off the main gas burner if the pilot should go out. The smoky gases arising from the burning garbage pass into the after-burning chamber H which is lined with firebrick. This lining gets very hot, and radiation from it helps to complete combustion. This is further helped by a fresh intake of air at this point from a weighted and hinged flap known as a draught stabilizer (not shown); this also has the function of controlling the amount of chimney draught.

It is scarcely possible to make an incinerator which will operate regardless of the nature of the material being burned; obviously, a wet parcel of cabbage leaves requires more heat than a bundle of newspapers. The operator has to judge how long it will be necessary to have the burner alight; then he sets the automatic timer accordingly.

GAS LIGHTING

As we saw in the first chapter of this book, gas when first introduced was thought of almost entirely as a means of illumination. For most of the nineteenth century gas lighting was the only artificial lighting available, except for the oil lamp and the candle. The gas which was made was specially intended to give a very luminous flame when burned, and indeed the standard of control at that time was not the heating value but the illuminating value of the gas. Quality was specified not in therms or calories, but in candlepower.

A great change took place in the last decade of the nineteenth century as a result of the invention in Vienna of the Welsbach mantle. Just about the time when the first incandescent electric lamp bulbs were being produced, Welsbach produced a fine-meshed pocket of what looked like a fabric, but which was really a network

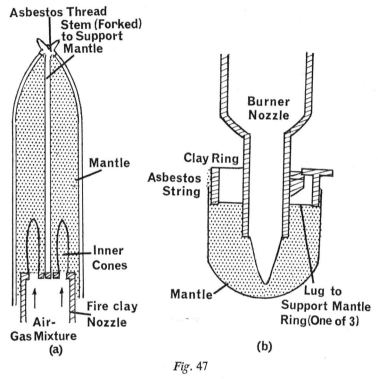

Fig. 47

of thorium oxide retaining the shape of the cotton fibres from which it had been made. The procedure was to make a mantle from some textile material, soak it in the nitrate of thorium (containing about 1 per cent of cerium nitrate[1]) and then heat the mantle to dryness;

[1] Thorium and cerium are relatively rare elements; thorium has a very high molecular weight and is slightly radioactive. Thorium oxide by itself has a low thermal emissivity and so reaches a high temperature when a flame plays upon it; however, it needs this 1 per cent of cerium oxide to make it glow brightly. Thorium oxide by itself (although very hot) gives out little light; the addition of cerium oxide (although lowering the temperature somewhat) greatly increases the light emission.

finally, it was burned. The nitrates were converted to oxides, the mantle shrank to about one half its original size, all the carbonaceous matter was burned off, and a mantle was left which retained the structure of the original fabric, but consisted solely of the two mixed oxides.

When a bunsen flame was burnt inside such a mantle, the result was a light which seemed brilliant at the time, and which completely outclassed anything which could be achieved by relying on the luminosity of a flame. In the first decade of the twentieth century the upright mantle (Fig. 47 (*a*)) was superseded by the inverted mantle (Fig. 47 (*b*)), and when these inverted mantles were put together in a cluster a still brighter light was obtained.

As we all know, the gas lamp has been largely superseded by the electric light today. This is due to several factors:

(*a*) Most important, the efficiency of conversion from electricity to light has steadily increased and was always far higher than that of the gas lamp.

(*b*) The fragility of the gas mantle, compared with the far more robust electric lamp.

(*c*) The amount of attention needed to keep a gas light in good order.

(*d*) The far greater ease of switching on—a gas lamp usually had a pilot flame, and then could be turned on quite easily; but the pilot flame represented a serious addition to the energy consumption, and the cost.

(*e*) As the gas lamp was a less efficient converter of energy, so more heat was liberated in relation to the amount of light; this was a severe disadvantage in some cases, and certainly hampered design.

Of recent years, the gas light has become of some importance again in connection with the L.P. gas industry. If a lonely cottage or farm or caravan is supplied with butane or propane from a cylinder, the incandescent gas mantle comes back into its own as the most practical and efficient light source (assuming electricity is not available).

For those who knew the Welsbach mantle in its hey-day, however, this is only a slight consolation. By 1930 gas lighting was being steadily ousted as an interior system, but retained a strong competitive position in street lighting. If one walked around the streets of London in 1930 one found most of them were lit by gas lamps, and in many districts great care was lavished on the street lamps to keep them in good condition.

For a while the battle seemed even, but the advent of the discharge lamp, in which an electric discharge through mercury or sodium vapour produced up to seven times more light than would be developed by an electric filament lamp, really made victory for electricity certain. Around 1940 the gas industry in Britain decided it would be a good policy to acknowledge defeat and cease the struggle. There are still gas lamps in London streets—and in many other big cities—but they must be looked upon as a dying race.

GAS METERS

Gas is normally measured by volume, rather than weight. Meters consist basically of a simple motor driven by the force of the gas; the motor has just sufficient power to drive a counting mechanism, and thus to indicate the volume of gas which has passed.

The older type of gas meter, and the one still used when a high accuracy is needed (in laboratories, for instance) is known as the wet meter. It uses a cleverly made cylindrical drum, divided up by partitions, and the whole rotates half-immersed in water. The partitions are arranged so that each compartment first fills and then empties as the drum revolves; the drum is driven round by the flow of gas, and no gas can flow unless the drum rotates.

For most practical purposes the wet meter has been superseded by the dry meter, in which two leather bellows are alternately inflated (see Fig. 48). As gas fills up one bellows, a lever is actuated which closes the gas inlet and diverts the gas to the other bellows; at the same time an outlet valve is opened to allow gas to leave the first bellows. In this way the gas flows continuously into first one, then the other, and all the while the lever mechanisms which work the valves are also operating a counter and dials on the face of the meter. The amount of gas which has flowed is indicated by the number of times the bellows have opened and closed, multiplied by their volume.

The dry meter is also a very old invention, and although a number of improvements have been made they have hardly affected the basic principle. For many years the meter case was made from tin plate, soldered by craftsmen; now this is being replaced by a cast aluminium casing. One design seems at first to have only one connection, instead of the two one expects to see! It is, of course, an illusion; the two gas ways run concentrically, and this simplifies the meter fixing. In the traditional type the connections were always made in lead pipe, to avoid putting a strain on the tin-plate casing. This custom is likely to disappear as newer types of dry meter come into general use.

If one wishes to measure a rate of flow with one of the meters we have been describing, a stop-watch or other timing device is needed;

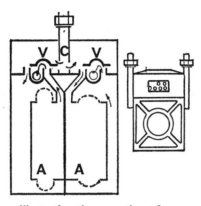

Fig. 48. Diagram illustrating the operation of a gas meter. The two valves V are linked together by levers which also operate the counting mechanism.

you observe the time taken for a given volume to flow, and so calculate the rate of flow in cubic feet (or cubic metres) per hour. There are however instruments available which will indicate the rate of flow direct. These usually depend upon a light float which moves in a tapered vertical tube. The tube is narrower at the bottom end, and so the annular space between the float and the inner surface of the tube is also at its narrowest.

When the gas flows up and around it, the float takes up a position in the tube where the pressure drop is just sufficient to sustain the float in place. If the rate of flow increases, the pressure drop also rises, and so the float is pushed upwards; it re-establishes itself higher up, where the annular gap is wider and the pressure drop is therefore once again equal to the weight of the float.

A scale is inscribed on the tube, and (provided that the density of the gas is known) the position of the float will indicate the rate of flow instantly. Flow meters of this kind are most useful, but they only give an approximate result, being less positive in action than the volume-displacement meters described earlier.

Gas is nearly always measured by volume, as this is far easier than attempting to assess the weight. There is however this disadvantage, that gas volumes vary with temperature and pressure in accordance with the well-known laws of Boyle and Gay-Lussac. A given parcel of gas, measured when warm, would register more than if it were cold; changes in the barometer also have a marked effect. When the barometer stands at Set Fair the gas will be compressed into a volume about 3 per cent less than if the barometer were at Rainy—and the user, in effect, gets 3 per cent more heat for the same registration on the meter. Such differences can be corrected for quite easily when gas is being measured on a large scale, but it is obviously not practicable to do so on the ordinary domestic supply.

Yet another kind of meter is used when large volumes of gas have to be measured. In this meter, two figure-eight-shaped members rotate together, in opposite directions—almost like gear wheels with only two teeth to each wheel. The effect is to provide a mechanism which can be driven much like a wet meter—that is to say, each rotation of the impellers corresponds to the passage of a known volume of gas. Unlike the wet meter, this relies upon metal members coming together with a very fine clearance gap; it is therefore not so positive in its action. It is however the best method of measuring the flow of gas at high pressure.

12 | The Future of the Gas Industry

Up to this point we have tried to give a factual account of the position as it is today. In this last chapter we must add some fancy to the facts, for we are going to attempt to suggest some of the ways in which the gas industry is likely to develop in the future. Obviously, this entails some guesswork, based on existing new ideas which it seems likely will become important in the future. However, forecasting the future is a chancy business and it is highly probable that some of the ideas which look promising now may, in the event, prove to be of little practical importance.

NATURAL GAS AND THE NORTH SEA

As far as Europe is concerned, the future course of the industry depends very much on the amount of gas which the exploration of the bed of the North Sea will yield. Judging by the results available as this book goes to press, it is not at all impossible that a vast reserve of natural gas comparable to the Texas Panhandle or to Groningen will be discovered. If that should be the case, the countries which border on the North Sea may by 1975 rely entirely on natural methane for their fuel gas supplies.

Even if this does not happen, the huge gas reserves of northern Holland will have a big effect on the surrounding countries. By about 1967 all the undertakings in Holland will be supplying their customers with natural gas, and by 1969 the same will probably be true of Belgium. Northern France and Germany would also provide a good market for Groningen gas, but there have been delays caused by protracted bargaining. Agreement has now been reached to export gas to Germany, and export to France seems likely in the future.

The future course of events will depend very much on the operations being conducted in the North Sea; after all, both Denmark and

Germany have their own corner of the Zechstein Sea bed to explore (see Fig. 7). Already some quite promising discoveries have been made in the area of the Ems estuary (including one actually in the estuary) and arrangements are being made to supply the big city of Hamburg with gas from this region. It is quite likely that in a few years' time enough will have been found to enable substantial quantities to be sent southwards to the industrial towns of the Ruhr and the Rhine.

LIQUID METHANE TRANSPORT

The future of liquid methane importation to Europe also depends very much on what the North Sea gives us. If it is generous, there will be less incentive to bring liquefied methane from afar. The traffic between Arzew and Canvey Island, and Arzew and Le Havre, will probably continue, as it is based on a long-term contract. The new methane routes however will be more likely to run towards those regions of the earth which have no gas of their own, or have exhausted their local gas fields.

It may well be argued that, to conserve natural resources, methane should in future be drawn mainly from existing oilfields. Gas which would otherwise be wasted could with advantage be sold at a low price, and this might make it economic to transport it in liquefied form from (for instance) the Persian Gulf, Iran, and Iraq. Where would it be sent to? Not to Europe, because Algeria, Libya, and even Nigeria are nearer. India perhaps might provide a market in the future. Venezuela is another country which burns large quantities of gas to waste—though less now than formerly—and it could reasonably expect to start selling to the United States before long. On the western seaboard the transport of liquefied methane from Alaska may become a commercial proposition when the indigenous supplies have become depleted. Before this time arrives, Japan (which has very little indigenous natural gas) may well be receiving liquefied methane from Canada.

In Africa, Nigeria has hopes of exporting liquid methane in the near future—presumably, to South America, South Africa, or to Western Europe. In Libya a large liquefaction plant is in course of construction on the coast. This will process some of the large amounts of gas which at present are being burned to waste in the desert a few hundred miles to the south. It seems safe to predict that most of this gas will before long be travelling by tanker to Italy, France, and Spain.

FROZEN GROUND STORAGE

The storage of methane in liquid form is not only a necessary stage in the transport of the substance by tanker; it may also be a useful method of holding gas for use at periods of peak demand. (The liquid only occupies one six-hundredth of the volume it would take up as gas at atmospheric pressure.)

The tanks as described in Chapter 6 are very expensive, but there is a new technique of making containers in frozen ground. For a large tank this is considerably cheaper, and also has the advantage that the liquid methane is stored wholly below ground level. A large cylindrical excavation is made in the ground; only the upper edge of the wall need be provided with a concrete lip, leaving most of the tank wall as bare earth. On the concrete lip is placed a well-fitting aluminium lid.

Before bringing the tank into use, the earth around it is chilled by a series of tubes carrying a refrigerant, such as cold liquid propane. This freezes the water in the soil and gives a hard surface to the tank wall; then liquid methane is allowed to run into it. The ice-bound soil is a barrier which effectively retains the cold liquid. As the thickness of frozen ground around the tank becomes greater, so the heat flow into it decreases. There will, of course, always be a certain amount of 'boil-off', but not more than with conventional surface tanks, it is thought. This gas is usually re-liquefied and returned to the tank.

It seems very probable that this will be the method of the future for storing natural gas in liquid form.

HOW LONG CAN THIS GO ON?

Finally we come to the very difficult question; "When shall we come to the end of our natural gas supplies?" If this book had been written about 1935 we should probably have replied, "About 1950; by then we shall have to find other means of making gas, probably from coal." Yet today, the known reserves are so huge that mankind may be fairly sure of drawing its fuel gas supplies from the earth up to (say) 2050 or perhaps 2100. Long before those dates are reached there will have to be extensive movements of gas over the surface of the globe, taking gas to regions in which the gas wells have become exhausted.

The forecasting is made much more difficult by our ignorance as to how much the rate of usage will increase. Hassi-er-R'Mel, for instance, could (it is thought) go on supplying gas to Britain at the present rate for 1000 years if it were kept solely for that purpose. Obviously, in the future the output will greatly increase, and the reserves will not last so long.

Nor do we know if mankind will gain sufficient control over his own planet to stop the wastage of natural gas which is going on at present at many oilfields (the amount being burned to waste in the Near East is about two and a half times the gas consumption of Great Britain). Finally, the whole subject is complicated by the lack of scientific knowledge on the origins and geochemistry of gas and petroleum.

In ten or twenty years from now we shall probably know a good deal more on this exceedingly important subject; exploration of the moon's surface, and deep drillings into the earth may elucidate much that is unknown at present. If, in addition to the gas of biological origin, the earth also holds large amounts of 'abiological gas', we may have a longer supply than seems likely now.

By the time the gas runs out we may reasonably expect to have solved the problem of producing power by nuclear fusion. This may lead to fuel gas playing a rather less important part in our lives. It seems safe to say that it will be still important as a chemical raw material, particularly for the manufacture of fertilizers—for we may reasonably suppose they will still play an exceedingly important part in human well-being.

PIPELINES

If this book had been written in 1961, a section devoted to future prospects would certainly have included some speculation on a possible pipeline from the Middle East to Western Europe, bringing to millions of European customers the gas now being wasted. Indeed, an American company prepared a quite detailed plan for such a pipeline—it would be no longer than some of the pipelines now in use in the United States of America.

There is, alas, no United States of Europe yet, otherwise this project might already have become a reality. Since 1962–63, however, the trans-European pipeline has become less attractive for a quite different reason; the wealth of natural gas in Holland and the likely discovery of still more under the North Sea. Gas seems now more likely to flow south-east to Austria and even beyond, rather than north-west from Syria and Turkey as originally contemplated.

Great pipelines will still be constructed, without doubt; there seems no reason to doubt the prosperity of this industry. How will future pipes differ from those we see today? Although steel is the only material used today, I find it hard to believe that it will always be used. Steel is heavy and easily corroded; aluminium presents big advantages in these respects. Even more attractive are the plastics materials, even though at present they cannot be used for very high pressures. Nevertheless, a glass-fibre reinforced epoxy-resin pipe is already in production which the makers claim to be as strong as steel—and, of course, vastly easier to handle. It is my personal guess that by 1985 plastics will be used for long-distance pipelines on a large scale.

Pipelines under the sea seem likely to be even more important in the future than in the past. The laying of these on the ocean bed would be greatly simplified if they could be made flexible, so that long lengths could be carried coiled on a drum. A project was prepared for linking Vancouver Island with the mainland by means of such a pipe; it was to be made of reinforced plastic hose. Not only would such a pipe make transport easier, but it would also accommodate itself to the profile of the sea bed without strain.

GAS MANUFACTURE

However much success attends the efforts of the seekers after natural gas in the North Sea, it seems unlikely that Britain will be able to do without gas manufacturing plant for some years to come. It takes some years to convert a gas discovery into a producing well. If the site be far from land, it will obviously take longer still.

Meanwhile the manufacture of gas from petroleum products makes great strides forward. It succeeds particularly well when it is integrated with an oil refinery. Then, by close collaboration it is possible to arrange that the gas-making plant takes for its use whatever petroleum product is least in demand by the public. Some re-forming plants can accept a wide variety of raw materials, and still produce a good gaseous product.

A plant of this kind, which probably indicates the path of future developments, is operated in England by the South Eastern Gas Board at the Isle of Grain, close to a very large refinery on the south bank of the Thames estuary. Refinery waste gases, petroleum fractions, and L.P. gases all come to the works by pipe direct, so that to a casual observer it would appear no work was going on at all.

At this works there are several re-forming plants, of different types, mostly producing a lean gas—largely hydrogen. This is enriched with hydrocarbons from the refinery gas and also from the stocks of L.P. gas (propane, butane, etc.). Another gas which is added is nitrogen; this is needed to make the gas mixture heavier, and therefore to resemble more closely the gas mixtures to which the appliances on the area of supply are accustomed. On each of these gas streams there are recording instruments which feed their information into a computer. The computer decides, from this information, in what proportion the gas streams are to be mixed, and opens or closes the valves accordingly. The result is an output absolutely uniform as regards calorific value and density.

On this works no gasholders are used, and the appearance is totally unlike the mental picture we normally have of a gasworks. By 1968 the output will be 170 million cubic feet of gas per day— nearly a million therms. This will be fed into a south orbital main which will run round the southern fringe of the metropolis carrying gas at pressures of up to 70 atmospheres.

The calorific value of the manufactured gas in the future will almost certainly rise, reaching an intermediate point between traditional town gas and natural gas. This is not only because these rich gases are cheaper to make, but because they help with the problem of delivering ever-increasing amounts of heat through existing pipes. In 1950 the gas made in Britain varied between 400 and 500 British Thermal Units per cubic foot (4500 kcal/cu. m). Today it is about 500 and by 1967 or 1968 may well be around 550–600.

THE GAS BURNER

Since it seems likely that in many districts the gas supplies of the future will be of natural gas, the makers of gas appliances are having to anticipate the event by providing burners and controls which can be used both on natural and on conventional manufactured gas. As we have just seen, manufactured gas is likely to rise in calorific value even if natural gas supplies do not materialize.

It is not possible to make an appliance which will pass from one kind of gas to the other without some adjustment; all we can do is to make a burner which can be easily converted—i.e., by simply changing over the injector nipple which controls the gas rate. Nothing we can do will eliminate the need to change to a smaller size of injector orifice if a gas of much higher calorific value is introduced. However, a so-called universal burner will operate with a minimum of alteration.

Methane and the other hydrocarbons all have a much slower flame-speed than coal gas—and this means that the hydrocarbon flame is less securely tethered to its burner. In Chapter 8 we compared the stationary flame to a man running down an upward-moving escalator, and so staying in the same place. In the case of hydrocarbon gases the man runs down at a much slower speed, so unless the escalator is also slowed down he will be carried rapidly up to the top and the flame will 'lift'. To slow down the escalator means, in practical terms, to enlarge the area of the flame ports so that the air/gas mixture flows out more slowly. This is all right for methane, but if the same burner is then used on coal gas the flame will probably flash back to the injector.

The designer of a universal burner has therefore to ensure that (a) the flame will be retained on the burner when methane is the fuel, and (b) the flame will not flash back when coal gas, or gas containing hydrogen, is burnt. Fig. 49 shows a burner of this kind, as used on a cooker hotplate. The flame ports are of two kinds; main ports A and subsidiary (low velocity) ports B. The gas comes out of the B ports so slowly that it produces a very stable flame which holds down the main flame at A. If the small ports were not supplied with gas, the flame would lift when burning natural gas, and probably float right off. On the other hand, when used with town gas the small ports B do nothing to hinder the normal operation.

It is safe to say that this type of burner, incorporating flame retaining ports, will become more common—perhaps universal. Correspondingly there will be fewer non-aerated jets (see Plate 15), because they are not suitable for use on hydrocarbon gases. Their loss will be a sore trial to the gas industry, for they represented (especially in the gas fire) a great advance over the aerated burner, which was always a little noisy and prone to block up from the sucking-in of domestic fluff with the air.

Now it seems that unless some brilliant invention is made the industry will have to return to the aerated burner. Little success has so far attended the production of a practicable non-aerated methane burner, but such would be extremely valuable if it could be devised.

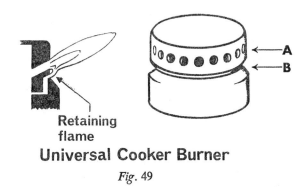

Retaining
flame

Universal Cooker Burner
Fig. 49

FUTURE GAS APPLIANCES

It seems likely that the use of electricity in gas appliances will be extended, and great possibilities will be opened up if collaboration between these two sources of power is fully developed. Already a great many gas-fired heating systems are dependent on electric power for their auxiliary equipment, such as circulating pumps, air fans, electric room thermostats, and sometimes even flame safety devices.

Cookers are now fitted with electric lamps and timing devices, and turning spits, and one British cooker has an electric oven with a gas hotplate. In industry, experiments are being made with a high-power aerated gas flame in which the temperature is boosted by the passage of electricity through the flame gases. By this means a much higher flame temperature can be obtained, which is very useful for certain special purposes. The amount of heat given out by a flame can be increased by three and a half times in this way; steel plate can be cut at express speed and even the element tantalum has been melted experimentally. This is one of the most refractory of all the metals, and its melting point, 3000°C, is far beyond what could be attained with an ordinary flame. Another possibility is that gas appliances of the future might use forced draught provided by an electric fan, thereby eliminating their dependence on the rather capricious and feeble forces of natural convection. As we saw in the last chapter, the use of natural convection necessitates a wide flue pipe, a draught diverter, and a flue pipe outside the building which may be expensive or unsightly or both.

This objection is partly met by the room-sealed, balanced-flue type of equipment, but on the other hand this means a considerable amount of building work and is in any case only feasible if the heater is to be fitted on an outside wall. If the flue gases were evacuated by means of an electric fan, it might be possible to use a 1-inch or $1\frac{1}{2}$-inch pipe in place of the 3-inch or 4-inch size needed at present. What an advantage that would be if a central heating boiler were to be fitted in the cellar of an old house! The 'pulsating combustion' technique which will be described in the next section affords one possible way of achieving this end.

Of course, such an arrangement would necessitate a safety switch to cut off the gas supply in the event of the current failing. The same principle might be applied to water heaters and possibly unit room heaters—might not the same fan which created pressure in the combustion chamber also blow air over the outside and provide forced-convection air heating?

In so far as hot-water circulation continues to be used for the heating of buildings (and warm air systems are not at all likely to displace it entirely) we may hope to see an end of the loop radiator, which is unsightly, dust-collecting, bulky, and not very efficient. By using more sophisticated techniques of heat interchange it is possible to deliver far more heat from a convector box which is considerably smaller. This type of heater will probably use an electric fan to blow air over the heated surface. It can also be designed to reduce greatly the wall-staining nuisance associated with the older radiators.

Another new development we may expect to see is the combined unit which provides circulating water to heat the house and at the same time a domestic hot-water supply for sink and bathroom. Some irritating difficulties exist which make this rather difficult at present. Water circulated continuously tends to become contaminated by rust, etc., and therefore unsuitable for supplying to a tap. Moreover, the continual introduction of fresh water to an ordinary central heating boiler would lead to the accumulation of scale on the heated surfaces. A third objection is that in summer time it is necessary to use the large boiler intermittently; cold air is drawn through the unit and this lowers the thermal efficiency.

However, there are several makers on the European continent producing water heaters to perform this double function. Sometimes a separate coil is incorporated for hot water supply; sometimes it is found practicable to use the same coil, by carefully choosing the point of draw-off. By 1975, one may conjecture, such dual-purpose heaters will be in general use.

PULSATING COMBUSTION

Pulsating combustion is a complete departure from conventional principles in gas appliance design. It has long been known that combustion takes place exceedingly rapidly under detonation conditions—i.e., in a mine explosion. If we could use detonation rather than the stationary flame we should therefore be able to achieve a much more rapid heat release in a given volume. This has been confirmed by experiment.

One of the very first attempts of this kind—made for a very different application—was in the flying bomb motor as used by the German air force in 1944. This used a resonating combustion chamber, so arranged that the force of each explosion projected waste gases out to the rear (giving the desired propulsion effect) and also sucked in a fresh supply of combustion air from the front. A simple flap valve prevented the explosive force from being thrown forwards. The burned gases then left along the only path open—that is, backwards—and their momentum was great enough to create a temporary suction, and so draw in fresh air from the front through the flaps.

It would hardly be expected that Londoners taking cover from these very frightening and destructive weapons thought they were seeing the prototype of a new peaceful application of gas heating! Yet this is a system which has considerable possibilities. It can provide a very small combustion chamber, leading to a very compact heating unit, and the products of combustion are expelled by the force of each explosion; this gives the forced evacuation considered earlier in this chapter, with all the simplification of flueing problems that go with it.

At present, it seems the noise produced is such a nuisance that it would need large and expensive silencers; these more than outweigh the advantage of the system. In another ten or twenty years it may be a practicable method.

THE TOTAL ENERGY SCHEME

We have been discussing the possibilities of a closer alliance between electricity and gas, but there is another technique now being developed in the United States which would make an electricity supply to the premises quite unnecessary. Factories working the 'total energy' scheme only take gas; this passes to an internal combustion engine either of the reciprocating type or in larger installations a gas turbine; this drives an electric generator to supply the whole building with electricity.

The beauty of this scheme is that the exhaust gases and cooling water from the engine can now be made to do additional work, either to heat or to cool the building (air cooling is very necessary in the hot summers experienced in this part of the world). One problem that one might expect to encounter in such a dual-purpose scheme is that the demand for electricity and the demand for heating (or cooling) energy might not balance one another, at any one time. An ingenious technique has been developed to meet this difficulty. When there is too much electricity and too little heating (or cooling) the surplus current may be used to provide heat or cold. More often, however, a supplementary gas heating system would be used. When the reverse situation takes place, and electricity is in short supply, the excess heat can be used to chill the air entering the turbine and thus increase the power output.

Air cooling, when it is on this scale, does not usually make use of the simple hydrogen–ammonia–water cycle described in Chapter 9. Instead, a power-operated cycle is employed, in which the evaporation is made to take place by a lowering of the total pressure. One successful American model uses a water and lithium bromide system. The cooling effect is obtained, as before, by the evaporation of a liquid; but in this case the liquid is water. The lithium bromide —which is a substance akin to common salt—serves to absorb the vapour and so create a vacuum in the cooling unit. The salt solution which is so formed is boiled to separate the water off again, and the steam is condensed to water, which flows back to the evaporation chamber. Thus the cycle is completed.

IGNITION PROSPECTS

One development which is urgently needed by the gas industry is a really simple automatic ignition. You can light a gas flame with a match, or you can maintain a pilot flame close to the burner; a more sophisticated arrangement (used greatly on cooker hotplates) is to have a central pilot flame serving a number of burners. In this case, a flash-tube connects the pilot flame with the burner. As soon as the flash tube becomes filled with an inflammable mixture from the burner, a flame travels along it and ignition is the result.

There are excellent flint-and-steel mechanisms, but they require adjustment from time to time. Electrical methods of ignition are being increasingly used; these depend either on a glowing wire filament or a sparking device. One very successful arrangement uses a platinum wire which can be connected to a dry battery. The relatively small current which flows warms the wire, and it then acts as a catalyst to cause oxidation of the gas on the surface of the wire. This heats the wire to incandescence, and the gas flame is lit.

All these arrangements are useful and valuable, but the ideal answer is one which has been almost within our grasp for twenty-five years or more, but still eludes us. This is the cold catalyst—the piece of platinum sponge which will ignite a flame without any electrical stimulation. Town gas and air meeting on the surface begin to combine, the pellet starts to glow, and in a short time ignites the flame. The housing is designed to prevent the flame from continuing to play on the platinum after the burner has lit—as that would spoil it.

Unfortunately, the platinum sponge absorbs other things from the air as well; water, grease, food vapours, almost anything that is around. Having absorbed these substances, it is less responsive to town gas, and either works very slowly, or not at all. So far it has not been found possible to equip gas appliances with cold catalyst ignition on a commercial scale. At present the possibility seems to be receding, for the possible coming of natural gas makes it even less attractive.

The catalytic effect of platinum depends on hydrogen, and if we lose this component from our gas we are likely at the same time to say good-bye to our prospects of ignition by cold catalyst. Unless a new methane cold catalyst is produced? Who can tell?

Index